Vincent van Gogh

Paintings and drawings
from the collection of the
Vincent van Gogh Foundation
Amsterdam

The Arts Council : Hayward Gallery
23 October 1968 to 12 January 1969

FOREWORD

The Arts Council has on two previous occasions been indebted to Ir. V. W. van Gogh for considerable loans from his collection of paintings and drawings by his uncle Vincent van Gogh for exhibition in this country. In 1947 a large Van Gogh exhibition was shown at the Tate Gallery and subsequently in Birmingham and Glasgow. In 1955, at the request of the Walker Art Gallery, Liverpool, the Arts Council sponsored a second exhibition which was first shown in that gallery and afterwards in Manchester and Newcastle upon Tyne. All these showings were visited by many thousands of people. It is, therefore, most gratifying that Dr van Gogh, as Chairman of the Vincent van Gogh Foundation, to whom the collection now belongs, should have agreed to a third request that he should lend a hundred paintings and a hundred drawings to form the second of the important opening exhibitions at the Hayward Gallery.

The only additions to the loans from the Foundation have come, with Dr van Gogh's consent, from the National Gallery, who have lent *Sunflowers* (1888), from the Tate Gallery, who own the *Chair and Pipe* (1888), and from the British Museum, who have recently acquired the magnificent drawing of *The Crau from Montmajour* (1888) in the de Hauke Bequest. The last is a companion drawing to one in the Foundation's collection which is included in the exhibition. To the Directors, Keepers and Trustees of these National Collections we are deeply indebted for these loans.

Mr Alan Bowness has compiled this catalogue and written the Introduction. We are also indebted to him for assistance in the selection of the pictures and installation of the exhibition.

For help in the preparation of the exhibition we are most grateful to the following: Dr E. L. L. de Wilde, Director of the Stedelijk Museum, Amsterdam, where the collection is exhibited during the summer months until the new museum of the Van Gogh Foundation is finished; Dr E. R. Meijer, Director of the new museum, and Mr H. W. Hamel, head of the Publications Department at the Stedelijk Museum; Mr J. B. Braaksma, Cultural Counsellor, and Miss A. Stenfert Kroese, at the Royal Netherlands Embassy in London.

Gabriel White
Director of Art

VINCENT IN ENGLAND

'I am looking forward very much to seeing London, as you can imagine', wrote Vincent Van Gogh to his brother Theo on 17 March 1873. Vincent was then a fortnight short of his twentieth birthday – on 30 March – and for almost four years had been employed by The Hague branch of Goupil & Cie, dealers in modern paintings, prints and photographic reproductions. He had completed the first part of his apprenticeship to everyone's great satisfaction, and was now being sent abroad for the first time to join Goupil's branch in London.

In a sense, one might say that it was in London that Vincent got his education – not a formal one, for Vincent was no scholar as he was later sadly to realize, but an education in life. He stayed for almost exactly two years on this first visit to London, and when he returned home he was a changed person: the cheerful, considerate boy had become a difficult, moody, depressed young man, unsure of himself and yet already obscurely feeling a creative drive stirring within him. Of course the change may have been inevitable – something that would have happened to Vincent in his early twenties wherever he had been. But I am inclined to think that Vincent's London experience gave it a particular quality that was to colour his whole life. Mid-Victorian London unsettled Vincent, and opened his eyes.

Vincent arrived in London some time in the latter half of May,[1] and at first all went well. Vincent's sister-in-law, Johanna van Gogh-Bonger, tells us that 'the first year of Vincent's stay in London was perhaps the happiest and most carefree time in his life. His salary [£90 a year] was large enough to live on, he felt great interest in his work and in all the new attractions that London offered him. . . .' (Introduction to London section of *Letters*.) He enjoyed playing the part of a successful young business man, buying himself a top-hat, – 'you cannot be in

[1] We do not know the exact date. He travelled from the family home at Helvoirt to Paris on Monday, 12 May, then 'spent some pleasant days in Paris' (9 – all numerical references in the Introduction are to the *Complete Letters*) before going to London. This first letter from London is dated 13 June: it mentions an excursion made with fellow lodgers at Whitsun (incorrectly translated as Easter in the English edition) which fell on 1 June in 1873, so he must have arrived sometime between 15 and 31 May. I would guess that it was at the weekend of 17–18 May, so that he could begin work on Monday, 19 May.

London without one'. He still had the country boy's wonderment at the size and wealth of London: 'One of the finest sights I have seen is Rotten Row in Hyde Park, where hundreds of ladies and gentlemen ride on horseback. In all parts of the town there are beautiful parks with a wealth of flowers such as I have never seen anywhere else.' (9a, 2 July 1873.) And writing a few weeks later he says: 'I have visited neither Crystal Palace nor the Tower yet, nor Tussaud's; I am not in a hurry to see everything. For the present I am quite satisfied with the museums, parks, etc.; they interest one more.' (10a, 7 August 1873.)

At that time Goupil's did not have an exhibition gallery in London, but an office and stockroom at 17 Southampton Street, off the Strand.[1] Vincent worked from nine to six, and up to four o'clock on Saturdays – not very demanding hours for those days – and he was probably chiefly concerned with selling to retailers Goupil's famous *Galerie Photographique* – photographic reproductions of popular modern paintings. He walked to and from his work: 'I used to pass Westminster Bridge every morning and every evening, and I know how it looks when the sun sets behind Westminster Abbey and the Houses of Parliament, and how it looks early in the morning, and in winter in snow and fog.' (32, 24 July 1875.)[2] We do not know the address of the first boarding house where he lodged: it was probably in the Clapham area: then a prosperous middle-class district. 'The neighbourhood where I live is quite beautiful, and so quiet and intimate that you almost forget you are in London. In front of every house there is a small garden with flowers or a few trees, and many houses are built very tastefully in a sort of Gothic style. Still, I have a good half-hour's walk to get to the country.' (9a, 2 July 1873.)

At eighteen shillings a week, washing excepted, Vincent found his idyllic suburban existence too expensive, and he moved in late August to the Clapham house[3] of Mrs Loyer, 'a curate's widow from the south of France, who with her daughter Ursula ran a day school for little children' (van Gogh-Bonger's *Memoir* printed in the *Letters*).

[1] In January 1875 the business moved to 25 Bedford Street, Strand, where pictures could be shown and exhibitions held. Among the first artists represented were the French landscape painters, Dupré, Michel, and Daubigny, and the Dutch painters, Maris, Israels, Mauve and Bisschop (22).

[2] Vincent is writing to Theo from Paris, and speaks of a painting by De Nittis, a view of London on a rainy day. 'When I saw that picture I felt how much I loved London.' Though he adds – 'Still, I think it is better for me that I left.' (32)

[3] Again we do not know the exact address. Vincent tells us it took him about three-quarters of an hour to walk home from Southampton Street.

The months that followed were the happiest of Vincent's life. He told Theo in January 1874: 'I am doing very well here. I have a delightful home, and it is a great pleasure for me to study in London, the English way of life and the English people themselves. Then I have nature and art and poetry. If that is not enough, what is?' (13) But he had fallen in love with Ursula, and didn't dare to confess it, until he was on the point of returning home for his Summer holiday – and then he discovered that Ursula was already engaged to the man who had boarded with the Loyers before Vincent came.

Perhaps Vincent never recovered from that first rejection. At first he did not accept it, and tried to make Ursula change her mind, but he had no success. Apart from this we know nothing about this first catastrophic attempt to build a stable relationship with the opposite sex. Vincent's consolation was twofold: art and religion, and they remained inextricably intertwined for the rest of his life.

We do not learn much about the next months from Vincent's own letters, but valuable information is to be found in passages of Johanna Van Gogh-Bonger's *Memoir*, which are based on extant but unpublished letters of Vincent's parents to their son Theo. Here we read that 'with this first great sorrow [Ursula's rejection] his character changed; when he came home from the holidays [25/27 June–15 July 1874] he was thin, silent, dejected – a different being. But he *drew* a great deal. Mother wrote [to Theo]: Vincent made many a nice drawing; he drew the bedroom window and the front door, all that part of the house, and also a large sketch of the houses in London which his window looks out on; it is a delightful talent which can be of great value to him.'[1]

Vincent had told Theo in a letter of 16 June: 'Lately I took up drawing again' (17), and many years later he wrote from Drente: 'In London how often I stood drawing on the Thames Embankment, on my way home from Southampton Street in the evening, and it came to nothing. If there had been somebody then to tell me what perspective was, how much misery I should have been spared, how much further I should be now.' (332, October 1883.)

Exactly when this refers to, we do not know – on 31 July 1874, Vincent had told Theo: 'Since I have been back in England [after his summer vacation], my love for drawing has stopped, but perhaps I will

[1] It is interesting to have this early evidence of what seems to have been Vincent's regular practice – when he moved to a new place, he needed to draw his immediate environment as a means of coming to terms with it. I think he probably drew or painted the view from the window of every room he ever lived in.

take it up again some day or other.' (20) Whether he began again later in 1874 or early in 1875 before he was posted to Paris is not clear: what is quite certain, however, is that Vincent's first serious drawing was done in London, and that when he was turned down by Ursula he drew a great deal.

He also became more religious. Johanna van Gogh-Bonger writes that, after his short Summer holiday at home, 'Accompanied by his eldest sister [Anna], who wanted to find a situation, he returned to London. He took furnished rooms, 395 Kennington New Road;[1] there, without any family life, he grew more and more silent and depressed, and also more and more religious.' And again: 'Letters home grew more and more scarce, and Mother began to think that the London fog depressed him and that even a temporary change might do him good: "Poor boy, he means so well, but I believe things are very hard for him now".'

Vincent was in fact temporarily transferred to Goupil's Paris office in October 1874, to his intense displeasure, and he was back in London again by the end of December, ready for the opening of the new gallery. By now he was more than ever a solitary, an eccentric, and his unsuitability for an art dealer's life was becoming increasingly obvious. But he was not drawing: he spent his evenings reading. Much of Vincent's time was devoted to the Bible, and to works of moral reflection like Michelet's *L'Amour* and *Joan of Arc*, and Renan's *Life of Jesus* – but he was also beginning to read the great Victorian novelists, and the religious sentiments of George Eliot's *Adam Bede* particularly appealed to him.[2] As the later letters show, Vincent became remarkably well versed in English literature and on the occasions when he wrote in English he handled the language with real feeling. Had his residence in England been uninterrupted, it is not altogether wild to imagine that he would have turned to literature rather than to art – one thinks at once of

[1] The published editions of the *Memoir* always give *Kensington* New Road, but this is certainly a misreading of the text: Vincent never lived in Kensington. The name Ivy Cottage is also added, but this again is, I believe, a confusion: Ivy Cottage was in Welwyn where his sister Anna was to find a situation with a family. Vincent visited her on 17 June 1876: this is mentioned later. The Kennington house was demolished at the end of the century: a G.L.C. school now stands on its site.

[2] George Eliot was the first novelist to make a lasting impression on Vincent. In Paris he read her political novel, *Felix Holt* – 'it is a book that impressed me very much' (51, January 1876), and the *Scenes from Clerical Life* – 'a very fine book . . . three tales, especially the last one, *Janet's Repentance*, struck me very much' (55, 19 February 1876). There are many other later references in the *Letters*.

Joseph Conrad, born four years after Van Gogh, and there was in fact a now forgotten Dutchman of this same generation, Maarten Maartens, who wrote his novels in excellent English.

This was not to be. About the middle of May 1875, exactly two years after his arrival in London, Vincent was again sent to Paris, for what were to be his last months as a picture dealer. His attitude towards the career that had been chosen for him was now one of complete indifference, and this inevitably led to his being given three months' notice by Mr Boussod, the managing director of Goupil's, to take effect from 1 April 1876.

The months in Paris were miserable ones, and Vincent's unhappiness comes through in his letters to his brother Theo. There is no doubt that he resented being sent to Paris and having to leave London – it is significant that his only intimate friend in Paris was a young Englishman, Harry Gladwell, also employed at Goupil's and sharing the same lodgings. Vincent gives a memorable description of Gladwell's uncouth appearance, but adds:

'He has a wholly ingenuous, unspoiled heart, and is very good at his work. Every evening we go home together and eat something in my room; the rest of the evening I read aloud, generally from the Bible. We intend to read it all the way through.' (42, 11 October 1875.)

Vincent was drawn increasingly to religion, and writes about the sermons he attended, evidently attracted by the new evangelistic spirit abroad.[1] This was perhaps one of the reasons that drew him back to England – at all events, on being dismissed from Goupil's his one idea was to find a teaching post in England. He knew now what he wanted to be – a teacher of the Bible – and this was the first step towards that aim.

It was not so easy to find a position, but at the last minute an offer came. Vincent tells his brother:

'On the morning before I left Paris, I received a letter from a schoolmaster at Ramsgate. He proposed that I go there for a month (without salary); at the end of that time he will decide whether I am fit for the position. You can imagine I am glad to have found something.' (59, Etten, 4 April 1876.)

[1] He seems to have attended services in a Protestant church, perhaps an English-speaking one. Writing from Ramsgate on 12 May 1876 he tells Theo, to whom he had sent some English hymn books, 'I am also so fond of that *Tell me the old, old story*. I heard it for the first time in Paris one night in a little church where I often went.' (66)

Vincent's second stay in England began on 16 April 1876 and ended at Christmas of the same year. He went first of all directly to Ramsgate, where a Mr Stokes ran a small boarding school on the seafront for twenty-four boys aged 10 to 14. Vincent and a 17-year-old boy were the assistant teachers – Vincent was responsible for teaching elementary French and generally helping with lessons and supervisory duties.

From the letters, Vincent seems to have been happy at Ramsgate, enjoying his work and the situation by the sea. But at Whitsun Mr Stokes moved his school to Isleworth, then in the country and not yet joined to London. He was happy to keep his Dutch teacher, but could pay him no salary – only board and lodging and some free time to give lessons.

Shortage of money forced Vincent to walk from Ramsgate to London – not entirely unwillingly, as Vincent enjoyed physical exercise and had once walked to Brighton during his earlier stay in England. He set off on Monday, 12 June, travelling via Canterbury and Chatham, and arriving in London on Wednesday evening. He spent two nights in London, one at Lewisham with the father of his Paris friend Harry Gladwell. At 4 a.m. on Friday morning he set off again for Welwyn, to spend the weekend with his sister Anna who was working with a family there. She had been in England since her arrival with Vincent almost two years before: she was very happy in Welwyn, and content to stay for a while. (69a)

As for Vincent, he realized that he could not remain at Mr Stokes's school, and he knew clearly what it was he wanted to do. 'If I should find anything,' he told Theo on 17 June 1876, 'it will probably be a position between clergyman and missionary among the working people in the suburbs of London.' (69) A few weeks before, writing to Theo about the English hymns, he had said: 'I am sorry indeed that I did not hear Moody and Sankey when they were in London. There is such a longing for religion among the people in large cities. Many a labourer in a factory or shop has had a pious childhood. But city life sometimes takes away the "early dew of morning". Still, the longing for the "old, old story" remains; whatever is at the heart's core stays there. In one of her novels[1] [George] Eliot describes the life of factory workers who have formed a small community and hold their services in a chapel in Lantern Yard; she calls it the "Kingdom of God on earth" – no more and no less. There is something touching about those thousands of people crowding to hear these evangelists.' (66)

[1] *Felix Holt.*

Vincent wanted to be an evangelist himself, a teacher of the Bible. Living in mid-Victorian London had made him aware of the lot of the poor – the great teeming industrial proletariat, overworked, underfed, badly housed, condemned to an existence without meaning. He already felt that he must identify with them, must bring to them the teaching of Christ. But how was the ambition to be realized? He wrote to Theo on 5 July:

'Lately it has seemed to me that there are no professions in the world other than those of schoolmaster and clergyman, with all that lies between these two – such as missionary, especially a London missionary. I think it must be a peculiar profession to be a London missionary; one has to go around the labourers and the poor to preach the Bible, and as soon as one has some experience, talk with them, find foreigners who are looking for work or other persons who are in difficulties and try to help them, etc., etc. Last week I went to London two or three times to find out if there was a chance of becoming one of them, as I speak a number of languages and have mixed, especially in Paris and London, with people of the lower class and foreigners. Being a foreigner myself, I thought I might be fit for it and might become increasingly so. However, one must be at least 24 years old, and at all events I shall have to wait another year.' (70)

Vincent had already written asking for help to an unknown clergyman whose church he had often attended during his earlier period in London. (69) Although he saw the gentleman concerned on 15 June, nothing seems to have come from the interview. He also applied for a position as an evangelist among the coal miners, but was told he was not old enough (126, 15 November 1878). However, between 5 and 8 July he moved from one educational establishment in Isleworth to another – leaving Mr Stokes for a similar small boarding school, Holme Court, in the Twickenham Road,[1] run by a congregational minister, the Rev. Thomas Slade Jones. Mr Jones was 47 at the time, and the school was a sideline to supplement his inadequate income. He was nursing a new parish in West London: he had purchased some land not far off in the Chiswick High Road where a new estate was being built, and in 1875 put up a temporary chapel, a 'tin tabernacle', while his church was erected. This was the Turnham Green Church, later to be called Gunnersbury Congregational Church.

[1] The site is now occupied by the Bear Honey factory. This information and the details of Mr Jones's identity and his activities come from a note, *Van Gogh in England* by John H. Taylor, in the *Burlington Magazine* for September 1964. Despite the title, the article deals only with Vincent's relations with Mr Jones.

Mr Jones took a real interest in Vincent, and sympathized with his ambitions. He allowed him to read the Bible with his schoolboys, rather than teach them French, and on 7 October Vincent writes:

'Mr Jones has promised me that I shall not have to teach so much in the future, but may work more in his parish, visiting the people, talking with them, etc. May God give it His blessing.' (76)

Vincent was already attending prayer meetings at a Methodist Chapel in Richmond every Monday evening, sometimes speaking on short texts, such as 'He has sent me to preach the Gospel to the poor'. (77) Mr Jones's support now made Vincent feel that at last he was overcoming his problems:

'I cannot tell you how glad I am that Mr Jones has promised to give me work in his parish, so that I shall find by and by what I want.' (76)

By October, Vincent was ready to preach his first proper sermon: he chose his text from Psalm 119: 'I am a stranger on the earth, hide not thy commandments from me.'[1] Under Mr Jones's patronage he was playing an increasingly active role in church affairs, and on 10 November tells Theo: 'A new assistant has come to the school, for in the future I shall work more at Turnham Green.' (80) At about the same time the Teachers' Meeting Minutes of Turnham Green Church record 'that Mr Vincent Van Gof be accepted as co-worker'. As well as at Turnham Green and Richmond, Vincent also preached at Petersham, where a similar wooden tin-roofed church had been erected.[2] His letters written at the end of the year show his complete absorption in this work.

Exactly why it came so suddenly to an end we do not know. Vincent returned home to Etten for Christmas 1876, and he never came back to England. Perhaps Mr Jones had to point out that Vincent was not qualified for a career as a Congregational Minister, and that there was no real future for him as a lay preacher and church social worker. Perhaps, too, he encouraged him to try and prepare himself for the Dutch Protestant Ministry, following in his father's and grandfather's footsteps. At all events he kept a paternal interest in his Dutch protegé, and when Vincent's theological studies came to such a disastrous end, it was Mr Jones who came to the rescue. He visited Etten in

[1] The sermon is published in full in the *Letters*, pp. 87–91 of the English edition. Apart from the choice of text it is not very revealing, though Vincent illustrates his points by quoting Christina Rossetti and describing a painting, *The Pilgrim's Progress* by G. H. Boughton.

[2] There are drawings of the Petersham and Turnham Green chapels in letter 82. Mr Jones made a speciality of 'tin tabernacles' and later wanted to put them up in the Borinage. (130, June 1879.)

July 1878, and took Vincent and his father with him to Belgium to introduce him to the School of Evangelism at Brussels. No doubt it was Mr Jones's advocacy that persuaded the School committee to accept Vincent as a pupil in August 1878, and this led in due course to his temporary nomination in January 1879 as an evangelist at Wasmes, near Mons in the depressed mining area of the Borinage. But Vincent's too Christ-like behaviour soon led him into difficulties with his superiors; and his determination to bring the Gospel message to the miserably poor miners was gradually eroded by practical difficulties, and by his own growing doubts about conventional religion.

As Johanna van Gogh-Bonger says in her *Memoir*, this was 'that saddest, most hopeless time of his never very fortunate life'. After the desperate winter of 1879–80, Vincent returned to Etten and spoke again to his father about going to London. 'If he really wants to go, I shall help him go,' wrote his father. But in fact he went back to the Borinage, and during the summer of 1880 he began to draw again and slowly realized that his true vocation was that of an artist.

Even so, Vincent's idea of what the artist should be was conditioned by these early experiences. Millet, who 'painted Christ's teaching', was always the painter he most admired, and Vincent himself remained a 'teacher of the gospel' to the end of his life. In the early part of his artistic career, his ambition was not to be a painter but to be an illustrator producing drawings of social comment for weekly magazines such as *The Graphic* and the *Illustrated London News* (288). Here again his debt to England was a strong and clear-cut one – his first taste in English art had been for Millais and his follower George Henry Boughton. Millais had helped inspire the black and white revival of the 1860s, and out of this had come the social realism of *The Graphic* which began publication in December 1869. The young artists associated with William Thomas's magazine – Luke Fildes, Frank Holl, Herkomer – were greatly admired by Vincent, who preferred them to Daumier and Gavarni because they really did 'something to arouse sympathy for the poor' (240). In December 1881 at The Hague he began to make a large collection of illustrations, mainly English, and the extent and nature of their influence on his work is still to be investigated.[1]

His first stay in England, 1873–5, came towards the end of the great

[1] I am preparing a study of Van Gogh and the English illustrators, in which I hope to discuss this question at length. Vincent's black and white collection – of several hundred sheets cut out and torn from magazines – remains uncatalogued and in the possession of the Van Gogh Foundation.

period of *The Graphic*, but the excitement of its weekly appearance was long remembered. Writing to his friend Rappard in early February 1883, Vincent said:

'I assure you that the *Graphics* I have now are amazingly interesting. More than ten years ago, when I was in London, I used to go every week to the show windows of the printing offices of the *Graphic* and the *London News* to see the new issues. The impressions I got on the spot were so strong that, notwithstanding all that has happened to me since, the drawings are clear in my mind. Sometimes it seems to me that there is no stretch of time between those days and now – at least my enthusiasm for those things is rather stronger than it was even then.' (R20, early February 1883.)

And of the English black and white artists, he says:

'... as I lived in England for fully three years, I learned much about them and their work by seeing a lot of what they did. Without having been to England for a long time it is hardly possible to appreciate them to the full. They have quite another way of feeling, conceiving, expressing themselves, to which one must get used to to begin with – but I assure you it is worth the trouble to study them, for they are great artists, these Englishmen.... For me the English black and white artists are to art what Dickens is to literature.[1] They have exactly the same sentiment, noble and healthy, and one always returns to them.' (R.13, September–October 1882.)

There is also no doubt that in this early part of his artistic career Vincent had at the back of his mind the iea of returning to England, if possible to work as an illustrator for *The Graphic*. Works like *Sorrow* and *The State Lottery* (Nos. 15 and 10) show us the sort of thing he was preparing himself to produce. It was only his increasing absorption with oil painting when he went back home to Nuenen in 1884–5 that led to a change of direction. And even so there is plenty of evidence in the letters that he had not forgotten England – he made English friends in Paris, like John Russell[2] and Alexander Reid, the dealer, and he looked to England as a place where his work might be appreciated. For example, we find him writing to Theo from Arles:

'My dear brother, if I were not broke and crazy with this blasted painting, what a dealer I'd make just for the impressionists. But there I am broke. London is good, London is just what we need, but

[1] The mention of Dickens reminds one that Vincent's links with English literature were also profound and would repay thorough investigation.
[2] Russell was in fact Australian-born, but this doesn't affect the argument.

alas I feel I cannot do what I once could. But broken down and none too well myself, I do not see *any* misfortune in your going to London; if there is fog there, well, that seems to be increasing in Paris too.

'. . . would it really be such great hardship to go to London -- if it is inevitable, is there any need to be miserable about it? After all there is no comparison; except for the climate, it is infinitely better than the Congo.' (513, *c.* 26 July 1888.)

* * *

Vincent never came back to England, and his three years here were spent in the early part of his adult life long before he had turned to painting yet perhaps enough has been said to show that this English experience came at a most impressionable age and helped shape Vincent's later development. One makes such claims not in any nationalistic spirit, but because there does seem to be some greater affinity between Van Gogh's approach and an English way of thinking and attitude to life than there is in the case of his great French contemporaries. In a curious fashion, Vincent is recognizably a great Victorian, whereas Cézanne or Monet or Gauguin or Seurat is not. He never loses a moral ardour, a humanitarian fervour, that they did not possess. The universality of his work that is experienced all over the world is perhaps intensified for us in just some way that makes it the more direct and personal.[1]

[1] All the relevant quotations from the Van Gogh letters have been collected together in *Vincent van Gogh on England*, edited by Dr V. W. van Gogh, and published on the occasion of this exhibition.

[illegible] I [illegible] do [illegible] once [illegible]. So [illegible] and [illegible] too [illegible] [illegible] [illegible]
[illegible] at Paris.

[illegible] great [illegible] to London [illegible] in [illegible] a [illegible] [illegible] the [illegible]

*

Vincent never [illegible] and his [illegible] were [illegible] of his [illegible] [illegible] though [illegible] to show that this [illegible] [illegible] not [illegible] [illegible] but [illegible] to [illegible] and [illegible] a great [illegible] [illegible] [illegible] [illegible] world [illegible] direct and personal.

[illegible] *Van Gogh* [illegible] edited by Dr V. W. van Gogh [illegible] and published on the occasion [illegible].

A NOTE ON THE CATALOGUE

The style of this catalogue follows that devised by Douglas Cooper for the 1948 London exhibition, and used again for the 1957 Arts Council exhibition, with certain modifications. All paintings, watercolours and drawings are now arranged in chronological order, and divided into seven sections. Each section has a short introduction, where the main biographical information will be found.

With three exceptions, all works belong to the Vincent van Gogh Foundation, Amsterdam, formerly in the possession of Dr V. W. van Gogh.

No full catalogue of the collection yet exists, but plate references are to the illustrated handbook.

Measurements given are in inches, with centimetres in brackets: height precedes width.

References are made to the existing complete catalogues as follows:
F = J. B. De La Faille, Paris and Brussels, 1928
H = J. B. De La Faille, London and Toronto, 1939 (an English edition of the foregoing: paintings only)
SA or SR = W. Scherjon and J. De Gruyter: *Vincent Van Gogh's Great Period*, Amsterdam, 1937 (paintings of Arles, Saint-Rémy and Auvers only).

Cooper = Douglas Cooper: *Drawings and Watercolours by Vincent van Gogh*, New York 1955.

A revision of the De La Faille complete catalogue is at present being prepared for publication by Mrs A. Telleghen-Hoogendoorn for the Rijksbureau voor Kunsthistorische Documentatie in The Hague.

The notes on each painting or drawing contain primarily the comments on the particular work (or subject) made by Van Gogh himself.

Numerical references here, and in the Introduction, are to the English edition of the *Complete Letters*, Thames and Hudson, 1958, with the translations occasionally modified. The dates added are those given by Jan Hulsker in his series of articles in the periodical *Maatstaf*, The Hague, between September 1958 and January 1961. If letters are added to the number, this is to indicate the recipient, e.g. LT means that the letter is written to Theo.

Some of the dating of the works themselves, especially in the Paris period, is tentative, and the suggestion of the compiler.

Alan Bowness

I EARLY DUTCH PERIOD

1853 March 30
Vincent Willem van Gogh was born in the parsonage at Groot-Zundert (North Brabant), the eldest surviving child of Theodorus van Gogh, pastor of the parish. Three of the pastor's brothers were art dealers. Vincent's mother, Anna, was a daughter of Willem Carbentus, royal bookbinder at The Hague.

1857 May 1
Birth of Vincent's brother, Theo.

1869 July 30
Vincent joined the Hague branch of the firm of art dealers, Goupil & Cie.

1873 May
Transferred to the London branch of the firm (see Introduction for details of Vincent's stay in London).

1875 May
Transferred to main Paris office of Goupil & Cie.

1876 March 31
Dismissed by M. Boussod, manager of Goupil's.

April
Began teaching at Ramsgate (see Introduction).
Working as teacher, lay preacher and church social worker at Isleworth, Richmond and Turnham Green.

Christmas
Returned home to Etten.

1877 January21–April 30
Worked in the bookshop of Blussé and Van Braam at Dordrecht.

May 9
Went to Amsterdam and began study with the hope of entering the theological faculty of the University.

1878 July
Abandoned studies, and returned home again.

August
Entered an evangelical training college in Brussels.

November
Went voluntarily to Wasmes, a mining village in the Borinage, South Belgium. Started a school, held bible lessons, was appointed a temporary lay preacher.

1879 July
Dismissed from missionary work for irregular behaviour.

August
Began to draw seriously: many copies after Millet, etc.
Slowly throughout a miserable and poverty-stricken year realized his vocation as an artist.

1880 October
Left the Borinage for Brussels, where he took lessons in anatomy and perspective. Met the wealthy art student, Anton Ridder von Rappard (1858–92), with whom he corresponded for the next five years. Began to receive a monthly allowance from Theo who was now working with Goupil & Co. in Paris.

1881 April 12
Left Brussels to return home to Etten. Disputes with his father about his career as an artist. Unrequited love for his cousin K. Many drawings of landscapes and peasants at work, in the manner of Millet.

December
Moved to The Hague, some tuition in oil painting from his cousin by marriage, Anton Mauve (1838–88).

1882 March
Met Christien (Sien) and set up an establishment with her family, which alienated his relations. Drawings and paintings of working-class subjects.

1883 September
Abandoned Christien and left The Hague to go to Drente, a remote province of North Holland, staying at Hoogeveen and Nieuw, Amsterdam. Some drawings and paintings of peasants, cottages, etc., but weather too bad to work out of doors.

December 2
Returned to the family house, now at Nuenen.

The De La Faille Catalogue lists nearly 300 drawings and watercolours, and some twenty-five oil paintings surviving from the early Dutch period. For much of this time Vincent was preparing himself for work as an 'illustrator of the people', and hoped to become a good enough draughtsman for *The Graphic* or *The Illustrated London News* or *L'Illustration*. Only at Drente at the end of this period does painting become more important.

1 The garden entrance

The Hague, 1872
Pen and pencil, 7¼x9 (18·5x22·5)
F836

One of a small group of early drawings (F839 shows the canal on the other side of the garden gate) done when Vincent was working for Goupil & Cie at The Hague.

The style is perhaps modelled on Corot drawings, and lithographs after Corot, with which Vincent was familiar from his print selling (see LT3).

2 The sower, after Millet

Plate 2

Etten, April 1881
Pen, heightened with green and white, 19x14¼ (48x36·5)
F830, Cooper 1

Vincent taught himself to draw by using Bargue's manuals and copy books (still in the possession of the Vincent van Gogh Foundation), and by copying etchings, engravings and photographs by and after the work of artists he admired. These were relatively easily obtained through Theo. His particular favourite was Millet, whose subjects – Sowers and Reapers, for example – had that symbolic religious significance which he hoped his own work would possess. Millet's visual images haunted Vincent's memory, and he frequently returned to them (see Nos. 140, 158, 166–8, 174, 177).

The Sower was drawn after a reproduction or a photograph (it is not reversed) of Millet's well-known painting. F830 is the only surviving straight copy of the subject, and, although usually said to have been done at Cuesmes in August 1880, is more likely to be the version mentioned in letter 144, see below.

Vincent wrote to Theo from the Borinage:

I must tell you that I am busy trying to sketch large drawings after Millet, and that I have already finished The Four Hours of the Day *as well as* The Sower. LT134, 20 AUGUST 1880

Everything you can find by that artist [Millet] *will be of the greatest use to me. I have already drawn* The Sower *five times, twice in small size, three times in large, and I will take it up again, I am so entirely absorbed in that figure.* LT135, 7 SEPTEMBER 1880

On his return home to Etten, he returned again to the subject:

I have been here a few days now and it is splendid outdoors, but the weather does not as yet permit drawing in the open air every day. Meanwhile I have started on the Millets. The Sower *is finished and I have sketched* The Four Hours of the Day. *And now I still have to do the* Labours of the Fields. LT144, 1 MAY 1881

3 Peasant digging

Plate 1

Etten, September 1881
Black crayon and watercolour, 24½x18½ (62·5x47)
F866

Advice received from Mauve after a visit to The Hague in August 1881 encouraged Vincent to experiment with new techniques and extend his subject matter.

... my drawing has changed, the technique as well as the results. Also, as a result of some things Mauve told me, I have begun to work from a live model again. Fortunately, I have been able to persuade several persons here to sit for me, Piet Kaufman, the gardener, for instance.... I have drawn five times over a man with a spade, a Bêcheur [Vincent uses Millet's word] *in different positions; a sower twice, a girl with a broom twice.... Diggers, sowers, ploughmen, male and female, they are what I must draw continually. I have to observe and draw everything that belongs to country life....*
I brought some crayon in wood (like pencil) from The Hague, and that is what I use most often right now. I have also begun to touch up my work with a brush and a stump, with a little sepia and India ink, and now and then with a little colour. LT150, SEPTEMBER 1881

I also had a model again a few times, a digger and a basket weaver. And then last week I received from uncle in Prinsenhage a paintbox which is still very good, certainly good enough to begin on (it is Paillard's paint). I am very glad to have it.
I at once started to make a kind of watercolour, like the sketch below.
[Sketch of F866.]
LT151, SEPTEMBER 1881

4 Donkey cart

Plate 4

Etten, September 1881 (?)
Pencil, heightened and washed with white, 15¼x23½ (38·5x59·5)
not mentioned in de la Faille

In letter 151 Vincent gives an account of his current work, which included *Peasant Digging*, No. 3. He added:

I am very happy to get models. I am also trying to get a horse and a donkey. LT151, SEPTEMBER 1881

The *Donkey Cart* may be the result.

5 Still life: a white cabbage with potatoes

The Hague, December 1881
Oil on paper mounted on wood, 13x22 (34·5x55)
F1, H2

One of Vincent's first attempts at oil painting, done when he was taking lessons from his cousin by marriage, Anton Mauve (1838–88):

I still go to Mauve's every day – in the daytime to paint, in the evening to draw. I have now painted five studies and two watercolours. . . . The painted studies are still life. . . .
Through Mauve I have got some insight into the mysteries of the palette and of water colouring. . . . Mauve says the sun is rising for me, but is still behind the clouds. . . . Sometime I will tell you more about how kind and considerate Mauve has been to me.
These are the subjects of two painted studies: a terra cotta of a child's head with a fur cap; and a white cabbage with potatoes, etc., around it.
LT163, *c.* 18 DECEMBER 1881

Vincent did not feel satisfied with these first efforts, and in January he stopped using oil paint to concentrate on drawing again. He did not paint another still life until nearly three years later (see Nos. 26 and 27).

6 Old woman walking, with shawl and stick

The Hague, February–March 1882
Pencil, 22½x11½ (57x29)
F913

A drawing based on a figure seen in the street, but probably modelled by Christien's mother, shortly after Vincent had met the family:

I have a new model now, though I drew her superficially once before. Or rather, it is more than one model, for I have already had three persons from the same family: a woman of forty-five, like a figure by Edouard Frère, then her daughter of about thirty, and a young child of ten or twelve. They are poor people, and I must say they are more than willing. . . . They have the right clothes. Black merino and a nice style of bonnets and a beautiful shawl, etc. . . .
Last night I went out with [Breitner] *to look for types among the people in the streets, so as to study them afterwards with a model. In this way I made a drawing like the above* [sketch of F913] *of an old woman I saw on the Geest, where the insane asylum is.* LT178, 3 MARCH 1882

7 Country road near Loosduinen

Plate 10

The Hague, March 1882
Black chalk and ink, heightened with white, 9½x13½ (24x34·5)
F1089, Cooper 4

On 10 March 1882, one of Vincent's art dealing uncles, Cornelis van Gogh (C.M.) visited the studio on the Schenkweg and liked a small drawing of the Paddemoes (the Jewish Quarter), F918. Vincent tells his brother what happened next:

Could you make some more of these views of the city? asked C.M.
Yes, I make them for a change sometimes when I am tired from working with the model—there is the Vleersteeg – the Geest [F914] *– the Fish Market.*
Then make twelve for me. LT181, 11 MARCH 1882

Vincent immediately set to work, though, as he told his brother:

I am decidedly not a landscape painter; when I make landscapes, there will always be something of the figure in them. LT182, 14/18 MARCH 1882

But he used this opportunity for studies in perspective construction, which he knew that he needed, and by 24 March had completed the 'little drawings' and sent them to C.M. (LT183).

Vincent interpreted 'views of the city' very freely, and No. 7 was probably one of this first series of twelve. It is evidently a finished drawing, suitable for public exhibition and sale, and because of the lack of foliage was more likely to have been done in March than later in the year.

8 Woman sweeping with a broom

The Hague, April–May 1882 (?)
Pencil and ink, heightened with watercolour, 19½x10¾ (49·5x27·5)
F1074

An unidentified drawing, but possibly one of the many studies modelled by Christien's family – in this case her mother – in April and May 1882.

9 View of Scheveningen

Plate 6

The Hague, July–August 1882 (?)
Pencil, white and black crayon, watercolour and gouache 17x23½ (43·5x60)
F1041

After the birth of her child Christien was too unwell to model for a time, and Vincent returned to landscape, working in particular at Scheveningen, the fishing village close to The Hague. He also wanted to start using water colour again after some months of drawing exclusively (LT219, 23 JULY 1882):

When you come, I want to try and show you some watercolours done in different ways. Then we can see and talk over which you think is best. . . . I have now made three of Scheveningen. . . .
You see I am quite taken up by landscape, but it is because Sien is not yet fit to pose; nevertheless the figure remains the principal thing for me. LT220, 26 JULY 1882

No. 9 has not been conclusively identified, but it is not altogether unlike F946, which is sketched in LT220, and it could well be one of the experimental watercolours done at this time.

10 The state lottery

Plate 5

The Hague, September–October 1882
Watercolour and gouache, 15x22½ (38x57)
F970; Cooper 6

Vincent wrote to Theo:

You remember perhaps Moorman's State Lottery office at the beginning of Spuisstraat? I passed there on a rainy morning when a crowd of people stood waiting to get their lottery tickets. For the most part they were old

women and the kind of people of whom one cannot say what they are doing or how they live, but who evidently have a great deal of drudgery and trouble and care.
Of course, superficially such a group of people who apparently take so much interest in 'today's drawing' seem rather ridiculous to you and me, because neither you nor I care in the slightest for the lottery.
But that little group of people – their expression of waiting – struck me, and while I sketched it took on a larger, deeper significance for me than at first.
For it is more significant when one sees in it the poor and money. *It is often that way with almost all groups of figures: one must sometimes think it over before one understands what it all means. The curiosity and the illusion about the lottery seem more or less childish to us – but it becomes more serious when one thinks of the contrast of misery and that kind of forlorn effort of the poor wretches to try to save themselves by buying a lottery ticket, paid for with their last pennies, which should have gone for food. However it may be, I am making a large watercolour of it.* LT235, *c.* 1 OCTOBER 1882

A rough sketch of No. 10 is included in the letter. The woman and baby in the right foreground were probably partly modelled by Christien and her child.

11 Old man, standing, with overcoat and stick

Plate 7

The Hague, October 1882
Pencil, 19¾x12 (50x30·5)
F962

Vincent found admirable (and inexpensive) models in the old men and women who lived in the almshouses at The Hague:

They call them very expressively orphan men *and* orphan women. . . .
I was interrupted while writing this letter by the arrival of my model. And I worked with him until dark. He wears a large old overcoat, which gives him a curiously broad figure; I think you would like this collection of old men in their Sunday and their everyday clothes. I also drew him sitting with a pipe. He has a queer bald head, large deaf ears and white whiskers. LT235, *c.* 1 OCTOBER 1882

I have made even more studies of the old men, and this week I also hope to have a woman from the almshouse. LT236, 8 OCTOBER 1882

I am doing a lot of figure drawing after the model and making sketches in the street. Besides, I have rather often had a man from the almshouse posing for me. LR13, *c.* SEPTEMBER/OCTOBER 1882

12 Old man in a top hat, half length

Plate 8

The Hague, October 1882
Black chalk, ink and wash, 23¾x14¼ (60·5x36)
F985

Throughout October Vincent worked hard at his studies of the old men and women:

This week I have drawn a few heads and also some children's figures and a few old men from the almshouse. LT238, *c.* 10 OCTOBER 1882

I am very busy working on drawings of an orphan *man, as these poor old fellows from the workhouse are popularly called here. Don't you think the expressions* orphan man *and* orphan woman *characteristic? It is not easy to do those characters one is always meeting in the streets.* LR14, *c.* OCTOBER 1882

13 Old couple, seen from behind

Plate 9

The Hague, October 1882
Pencil, 19¾x12¼ (50x31)
F991

The house continues to please me, except that one wall is very damp.
I can work here with a model much better than at the other studio.
I can even work with several people at the same time, for instance, two children under an umbrella, two women standing talking, a man and woman arm in arm, etc. LT238, *c.* 10 OCTOBER 1882

14 Old man weeping

The Hague, November 1882
Pencil, 19½x12 (50x30·5)
F997

The pose was one which first attracted Vincent at Etten, when he drew Schuitemaker, 'an old sick farmer sitting on a chair near the hearth, his head in his hands and his elbows on his knees' (LT150, SEPTEMBER 1881, referring to F863). He took up the subject again at The Hague:

Today and yesterday I drew two figures of an old man who is sitting with his elbows on his knees and his head in his hands. Long ago Schuitemaker sat for me and I always kept the drawing, because I wanted to make a lithograph of it. How beautiful is such an old workman, with his patched fustian clothes and his bald head. LT247, 24 NOVEMBER 1882

Vincent made a painting after this drawing when he was in Saint-Rémy.

15 Sorrow

The Hague, November 1882
Lithograph, 15x11¼
F1655

Sorrow – the English title was always used – is a good example of what Vincent thought would be suitable for the English illustrated newspapers for which he hoped to work.

This lithograph is based on two drawings (F929 and 929 *bis*), made in April 1882 (LT186). Underneath F929 *bis* is written: 'Comment se fait-il qu'il y ait sur la terre une femme seule délaissée', a quotation from Michelet. The model was the prostitute Sien. In all, Van Gogh made only nine lithographs, though at this period he was greatly interested in the process

16 Coffee drinker

The Hague, November 1882
Lithographic crayon, 16¾x8½ (42·5x21)
Not mentioned in de la Faille
A study for the lithograph, F1657

17 Old fisherman in a sou'wester

The Hague, January 1883
Pencil, ink and wash, heightened with white, 20x12½ (50·5x31·5)
F1014

Vincent liked to leave The Hague for the neighbouring village of Scheveningen:

I am very hard at work. . . . Tomorrow I get a sou'wester for the heads. Heads of fishermen, old and young, that's what I have been thinking of for a long time, and I have made one already, then afterward I couldn't get a sou'wester. Now I shall have one of my own, an old one over which many storms and seas have passed. LT261, *c.* 21 JANUARY 1883

I am very glad to have my sou'wester; I wonder if you will find some good in those fishermen's heads. LT262, late JANUARY 1883

18 Cottages at Drente

Plate 12

Drente, October–November 1883
Oil on canvas on pasteboard, 15x23 (36x55·5)
F17, H25

On his short visit to North Holland, Vincent was attracted less by the landscape or the peasants at work than by the characteristic mud cottages which he frequently drew and painted.
Much later he told Emile Bernard:

The most admirable thing I know in the domain of architecture is a rural cottage with a moss-covered thatched roof and a blackened chimney. LB20, late OCTOBER 1889

No. 18 is not mentioned directly in any letter from Drente, though the board on which it is painted is exactly the same size at that used for F22, *The Cottage*, which we know Vincent was painting in November (LT339).

II NUENEN

1883 December
Returned to the family house, now at Nuenen, in the eastern part of North Brabant.

1884 January
Nursed his mother, in bed with a fractured thigh bone.

Summer
Affair with one of three sisters next door, Miss Begeman, ended in her attempted suicide. Contacts with collectors and amateur painters in nearby Eindhoven.

1885 March 27
Death of Vincent's father.

November 27/28
Left Nuenen for Antwerp.

During the Nuenen period, Vincent made nearly 200 paintings and over 200 drawings. The subject matter was almost always drawn from peasant life, showing men and women at work and at rest (*The Potato-Eaters*), the objects they used or the landscape they inhabited. Vincent's ambition to be an 'illustrator of the people' receded with his growing interest in oil painting. There is much discussion of colour theories in the letters of 1885. It became more and more necessary to leave Holland.

19 Coming out of church at Nuenen

Plate 19

Nuenen, January 1884
Oil on canvas, $16\frac{1}{8}$x$12\frac{5}{8}$ (41x32)
F25, H29

On 17 January 1884, Vincent's mother broke her thigh on getting off the train at Helmond. The accident gave Vincent the opportunity of acting the helpful son, and this improved relations with his parents. He was an excellent nurse:

Taking her difficult situation into consideration, I am glad to say mother's spirits are very even and bright. And she is amused by trifles. The other day I painted for her the little church with the hedge and the trees (like this).
LT355, *c.* 24 JANUARY 1884

The sketch in Vincent's letter shows No. 19, but with only a single figure in the foreground. The others may have been added later. The church is the Protestant chapel, built in the 1820s, in a predominantly Catholic area.

20 The parsonage at Nuenen

Plate 17

Nuenen, January 1884
Oil on canvas, 13x16¾ (33·5x43·5)
F182, H199

This painting of the house in which Vincent's parents lived, with the laundry room which he used as a studio on the right, has traditionally been dated to the *end* of the stay at Nuenen. It is, however, so close to a sketch in letter 344, written 3/4 December 1883, and to a pen drawing (F1343) which was probably done early in 1884, that a date at the very beginning of the Nuenen period seems more probable. Vincent often drew or painted his immediate surroundings soon after his arrival at a place, and this painting of the parsonage consorts happily in size, subject and style with the painting of his father's church, No. 19.

21 The weaver at his loom

Plate 21

Nuenen, February 1884
Pen, heightened with white, 15¼x20¾ (30·5x40·5)
F1123

Vincent had wanted to paint weavers ever since he had seen the 'villages of the weavers' during his stay at Wasmes in the Borinage. At the time he wrote to Theo:

The miners and the weavers still constitute a race apart from other labourers and artisans, and I feel a great sympathy for them. I should be very happy if some day I could draw them, so that those unknown or little-known types would be brought before the eyes of the people. The man from the depth of the abyss, de profundis – *that is the miner; the other, with his dreamy air,*

somewhat absent-minded, almost a somnambulist – that is the weaver.
LT136, 24 SEPTEMBER 1880

The opportunity came when he returned to live with his parents, now established at Nuenen, and between January and July 1884 Vincent made at least ten paintings and seventeen drawings and watercolours of weavers, seated at their looms, in gloomy Rembrandtesque interiors. He made some watercolours first (LT351, early JANUARY), then some painted studies (LT355, *c.* 24 JANUARY), and in February five pen and ink drawings:

which I drew after my painted studies, and which are a little different, and I think more vigorous of technique, than the pen drawings of mine you have seen up to now. I am working at them early and late....
LT357, 13 FEBRUARY 1884

No. 21 probably belongs to this group of five; the composition is close to a sketch in LT355, *c.* 24 JANUARY 1884, in which Vincent writes:

Every day I am busy painting *studies of the weavers here.... These subjects of the looms, with their rather complicated machinery, with a figure sitting in the middle, will also lend themselves to pen drawings, I think, and I will make some....*

The painted study referred to may be F29, or a smaller version; the watercolour of the same composition is F1107, certainly done in January 1884.

Vincent explained at length to his painter friend Rappard that he began by wanting to make a mechanical drawing of the loom – *that monstrous black thing of grimed oak with all those sticks* – but was compelled to include the figure operating it – *a black ape or goblin or spook that clatters with those sticks from early morning till late at night.*

When I had finished drawing the apparatus pretty carefully, I thought it was so disgusting that I couldn't hear it rattle that I let the spook appear in it.... And – if you were to put my study beside the drawing of a mechanic who had designed a weaving loom – mine would express more strongly that the thing is made of oak grimed by sweaty hands, and looking at it ... you could not help thinking occasionally of the workman, *whereas absolutely nothing like it would occur to your mind when you looked at the model of a loom drawn by a mechanic. A sort of sigh or lament must issue from that contraption of sticks now and then.* LR44, MARCH 1884

22 The garden of the parsonage at Nuenen in winter

Plate 22

Nuenen, late February–early March 1884
Pen and pencil, 15¼x20¾ (39x53)
F1128

One of the three early Winter Garden drawings (F1130 is another), made in the close vicinity of his parents' home; Nuenen old tower is seen in the distance.

Vincent sent them first to Rappard, who responded favourably:

Well I was pleased to hear that you liked my winter garden a little. Indeed, this garden sets me dreaming, and since then I have made another one of the same subject, also with a little black spook in it, not as an example, worthy of imitation, of the correct drawing of the structure of the human body, but as a contrast. LR44, mid-MARCH 1884

Vincent tells Theo that Rappard still has *the first three* Winter Gardens *which he also liked very much* (LT364, *c.* 1 APRIL 1884); he returns to the subject a few weeks later when the trees are in blossom:

I am enclosing a sketch of a picture which is one of those I'm working on; this is an afternoon effect of trees in blossom. There are three on the same subject you will get as soon as Rappard comes here; what struck me in reality was the remarkably quaint, half old-fashioned, half rustic character of that garden. LT366, APRIL 1884

The sketch in the letter shows a similar composition to No. 22 but no finished picture of this subject is known.

23 Pollarded willows, with shepherd

Plate 27

Nuenen, March 1884
Pen and pencil, 15¾x21½ (39·5x54·5)
F1240

With several other drawings, this one and No. 24 were sent to Rappard for criticism after he had expressed his admiration for the Winter Garden drawings (No. 22). They are mentioned by name in letter R44, written mid-March 1884, certainly before T364, which Hulsker dates 1 April. (LR44 in fact probably precedes LR43 in sequence).

24 Poplar avenue

Nuenen, March 1884
Pen and black crayon, 21¼x15½ (54x39)
F1239

See note to preceding entry.

25 Pines in the fen

Plate 3

Nuenen, March 1884
Pen, some pencil 14x17¼ (34·5x44)
F1249

Another of the pen drawings (cf. Nos. 22, 23 and 24), sent to Rappard for his comments:

A few days ago I sent you three more pen and ink drawings, Little Ditch [F1243], Pines in the Fen [No. 25], Thatched Roofs [F1242]; *I thought you would like the subjects. As for the execution, I should have wished with all my heart that the direction of the pen scratches had followed the forms more expressively, and that the forces which render the tone of the masses expressed their shape more clearly at the same time. I think you will admit that I did not systematically or intentionally neglect the composition of things, their shape, but I had to take a shot at it in a rough sort of way in order to render the effect of light and brown – the atmosphere of the scenery as it was at that moment – the general aspect as well as I could.* LR45, APRIL (?) 1884

26 Farmer's boy, standing

Nuenen, 1884 (?)
Pencil, 12¼x6¼ (31x16)
Not mentioned in de la Faille
This small drawing was given by Mrs Van Gogh-Bonger to a relative in *c.* 1900, and has recently been repurchased by the Van Gogh Foundation. It is said to belong to the Nuenen period, but may have been done in The Hague as early as October 1882.

27 Still life: three bottles, earthenware pot and bowls

Plate 18

Nuenen, November–December 1884
Oil on canvas on wood, 17¾x22 (40·5x56)
F53, H65

I now have three people in Eindhoven who want to learn to paint, and whom I am teaching to paint still life. LT385, NOVEMBER 1884

The Eindhoven amateurs were Hermans, Van de Wakker and Anton Kerssemakers, a tanner about forty years old who became Vincent's friend and most devoted pupil, paying him with tubes of paint:

We set to work at once. So that very evening he had already brushed a still life, and he has promised me he will try to paint about thirty of them this winter, which I will come and look at now and then, and help him to make. LT386, before 20 NOVEMBER 1884

Vincent had not attempted still life painting since his first unsuccessful efforts for Mauve (e.g., No. 5) in December 1881, but now began to do some for his own satisfaction, using objects provided by his pupils (LT387). No. 27 is probably one of the earliest of a group of almost twenty still lifes done at this time.

28 Still life: copper pan, jug and potatoes

Nuenen, November–December 1884
Oil on canvas, 26x32 (66x81)
F51, H55

See note to preceding entry. The copper pan was probably one of the objects owned by Hermans, the goldsmith, which Vincent was allowed to take to his own studio to work from. (LT387)

29 Head of a peasant woman, with Brabant headdress

Nuenen, December 1884–January 1885
Oil on canvas on pasteboard, 16¾x13½ (42·5x34)
F156, H140

A series of English illustrations which particularly appealed to Vincent was Herkomer's *Heads of the People Drawn from Life*, and he began to draw his own series when in The Hague. He didn't get very far at the time, but when Rappard visited him in Nuenen in October 1884 the idea must have been discussed again. Rappard wanted Vincent to join him in Antwerp, but there would be money problems:

But in general, Rappard too advises me to do it, not right away, but after having painted here for a few more months, then to try to get a pied-à-terre there to paint some studies from the nude. But if I paint about thirty studies of heads here first I shall be able to get more out of Antwerp, and I am starting on those thirty heads now, or rather I have already done so, along with a large bust of a shepherd. LT383, OCTOBER 1884

There was, however, the problem of finding 'suitable models, of just the type I want (rough, flat faces with low foreheads and thick lips, not sharp, but full and Millet-like)' (LT372) – and also of finding money to buy paint and pay the models. So Vincent's progress at first was slow, and interrupted by the sequence of still lifes painted in November (see Nos. 27, 28). He was now planning a larger series: he had already told his brother on 1 November:

Look here now – I must paint fifty heads just for experience, because right now I am hitting my stride. As soon as possible and one after the other. LT384

By 14 December he had made a start, and could send Theo sketches of the paintings:

I must make about fifty of those heads while I am still here, and while I can get, relatively easily, all kinds of models during the winter months. But now if I don't take care, the winter months will pass without my making as many as I want and as are necessary.... By working on steadily, those fifty heads will be finished this winter. But they require so much work and drudgery that I can't spare a day. LT389, 14 DECEMBER 1884

A few days later Vincent wrote again:

I'm working very hard on the series of heads from the people which I have set myself to make. I'm just enclosing a little scratch of the last one; in the evening I generally sketch them from memory on a little scrap of paper, this is one of them. Perhaps later I will make them in watercolour too. But first I must paint them. LT390, mid-DECEMBER 1884

On 1 January 1885 he writes:

In two or three days you will receive twelve little pen and ink drawings after studies of heads.... I feel most in my element when I am working on the figure.... I don't yet know what I shall do with those heads, but I want to extract the motif from the characters themselves. But I know quite well why I made them, and what in general I have in mind. LT391, 1 JANUARY 1885

Despite running out of money at the end of the month, and begging Theo for more help in paying models, Vincent continued:

I am very busy painting those heads. I paint in the daytime and draw in the evening. In this way I have already painted at least some thirty and drawn as many. . . . I think it will help me for the figure in general.

Vincent goes on to say that he is looking for touches of blue to contrast with 'the golden tones of reddish-brown'. He continues:

But this is a question of colour, and what matters more to me at the point I'm at now is the question of form. I think the best way to express form is with an almost monochrome colouring, the tones of which differ principally in intensity and in value. LT394, FEBRUARY 1885

Vincent continued the series during March and April, sometimes more consciously exploiting colour contrast effects (LT397), as his own interest in colour theory rapidly developed. But he was now ready for the more ambitious compositions that arose out of the series, *The Potato-Eaters* (No. 38) and the scenes from rural life (LT400). These took up much of his time, but he was still adding to the series in May – as when after reading Zola's *Germinal* he painted another with an 'even stronger soft soap and brassy effect'. (LT410)

It is not yet possible to arrange the forty or so painted heads in a chronological order, and only a few can be exactly dated with certainty. No. 29 probably comes in the middle of the series.

30 Head of a peasant woman, 'with big white cap'

Plate 13

Nuenen, December 1884–March 1885
Oil on canvas on wood, 16¾x13⅜ (42·5x34)
F130, H137

One of the series of *Heads of the People*, see No. 29. This is the picture sketched and mentioned in LT397 as a suitable pendant for No. 37. It may possibly be the 'young woman's head' which Vincent tells Theo he will send him on 1 March 1885. (LT395)

31 Study of three hands, two holding a fork

Plate 23

Nuenen, January–February 1885
Black crayon, 8x13 (20x33)
F1161

A study for *The Potato-Eaters* (No. 38): the male and female figures on the left each hold a fork, and the clenched fist belongs to the woman seated on the right.
On the verso of this sheet is a study of the back wall of the Potato-Eaters cottage, with door and window; and a tiny sketch of the final complete composition.

32 Head of a young peasant, with a pipe

Nuenen, January–February 1885
Pencil and watercolour, 15⅜x11¼ (39x28·5)
F1199

One of the series of *Heads of the People*, see No. 29. This may be the same model as in No. 34.

33 Head of a peasant woman, with close-fitting white cap

Plate 24

Nuenen, January–April 1885
Pencil and charcoal, 13¼x8¼ (33·5x21)
F1184

One of the series of *Heads of the People*, see No. 29. This may be the same model as in No. 37.

34 Head of a young peasant, with a pipe

Nuenen, January–April 1885
Oil on canvas on pasteboard, 15x12 (38·5x30·5)
F164, H184

One of the series of *Heads of the People*, see No. 29. Male portraits are relatively uncommon, although one is mentioned in LT398 of April 1885, and No. 34 seems stylistically late in the series.

35 Peasant woman sewing

Nuenen, March 1885
Oil on canvas on pasteboard, 17¼x13½ (43·5x34·5)
F71, F78

When he had almost achieved his aim of painting fifty *Heads of the*

People, Vincent began to think of putting his studies to use. He must by now have felt ready to paint a picture suitable for public exhibition. He writes to Theo:

I am brooding over a couple of larger, more elaborate things, and if I should happen to get a clear idea of how to reproduce the effects I have in mind, in that case I should keep the studies in question here for the time being because I should certainly need them – it would be, for instance, something like this: namely figures against the light of a window. [Sketch in letter] *I have studies of heads for it, against the light as well as turned towards the light, and I have worked several times already on the complete figure; spooling yarn, sewing, or peeling potatoes. Full face and in profile, it is a difficult effect.* LT396, mid-MARCH 1885

No. 35 is probably one of these first painted studies of the complete figure; it has the against-the-light effect that interested Vincent. But he gave up the idea of a composition of women seated working inside a cottage in favour of *The Potato-Eaters*.

36 Still life with honesty

Nuenen, March 1885
Oil on canvas on pasteboard, 16½x12¾ (42·5x32·5)
F76, H81

Vincent's father died suddenly on 27 March 1885. He wrote to Theo:

I am still greatly under the impression of what has just happened – so I have worked on quietly these two Sundays [i.e., he has not written to Theo, as was his Sunday practice].
Enclosed you will find a sketch of a man's head, and of a still life with honesty, in the same style as the one you took with you; in the foreground are Father's tobacco pouch and his pipe. LT398, mid-APRIL 1885

No. 36 is not the still life with honesty sketched in the letter – this has not been traced and was probably destroyed. But it may be the still life Theo took away with him, when he came home for their father's funeral: this was the *still life of those honesties and leaves against blue* which was admired by uncle Cor, Vincent tells us in letter 397 (very early April). These are the first still life paintings in which Vincent uses objects for their symbolism, an idea he developed remarkably later in the year (see Nos. 51, 52 and 53).

37 Head of a peasant woman, with red kerchief

Nuenen, April 1885
Oil on canvas, 16½x11½ (43·5x30·5)
F160, H159

One of the series of *Heads of the People*, see No. 29, this can be precisely dated because Vincent sketches it in a letter of April 1885 and says:

The head I painted today is, I think, as good as the one with the big white cap which you have; it is somewhat like this sketch, and might serve as a pendant to it.

If you mounted these two on gilt Bristol, they would perhaps look well in gold, better than without it. LT397

The pendant is No. 30

38 The potato-eaters

Plate 15

Nuenen, late April–early May 1885
Oil on canvas, 32x45 (81x114)
F82, H plate 1

The Potato-Eaters is Vincent's largest figure painting, and the culmination of his work as a Dutch peasant painter. It is a picture firmly in the tradition of Millet and the Barbizon School, which for Vincent in 1885 represented the mainstream of modern art. Millet's contemporary in Holland was Jozef Israels, for Vincent the greatest living Dutch painter (LT408), and Israels *Frugal Meal* (Glasgow) of 1884 provides the immediate precedent for *The Potato-Eaters*. Goupil's, Theo's firm, produced a reproduction of Israel's picture in 1884, and it is even possible thatTheo may have brought a print with him when he returned for his father's funeral at the end of March 1885.
Whatever its exact origins, we know Vincent had for some time been thinking about starting work on a more ambitious picture (see note to No. 35), although the first precise reference comes in mid-April:

This week I intend to start that composition of those peasants around a dish of potatoes in the evening, or – perhaps I shall make daylight of it, or both, or 'neither of the two' you will say. But whether it may succeed or not, I am going to begin studies for the various figures. LT398, APRIL 1885

The first idea may be seen in a small painting (F77, measuring 13x18) belonging to the Vincent van Gogh Foundation.

A few days later Vincent wrote again:

I am again working on those peasants around a dish of potatoes.
I have just come home from this cottage and have been working at it by lamplight, though I began it by daylight this time.
This is what the composition looks like [written underneath a sketch].
I painted it on a rather large canvas, and as the sketch is now, I think there is some life in it. LT399, APRIL 1885

The painting here referred to is the picture now in the Kröller-Müller Museum (F78, measuring $28\frac{1}{4}$x$36\frac{3}{4}$) – sometimes confusingly called the second version, because it is in fact the large study which *preceded* the definitive version. Vincent was not even sure whether he would make a definite picture of the sketch . . . which we could send to an exhibition (LT401) until late in April, but once decided he went ahead with it quickly, hoping to have it ready to send to Paris for Theo's birthday on 1 May. He wrote on 30 April:

I should have liked to send you the picture of The Potato-Eaters *on that day, but though it is getting on well, it is not quite finished yet.*
Though the final picture will have been painted in a relatively short time and for the greater part from memory, it has taken a whole winter of painting studies of heads and hands.

Vincent continues by asking that it should be seen against gold:

on a wall, papered in the deep colour of ripe corn. It simply cannot be seen without such a setting.

He continues:

I have tried to emphasize that those people, eating their potatoes in the lamplight, have dug the earth with those very hands they put in the dish, and so it speaks of manual l*abour, and how they have honestly earned their food.*
I have wanted to give the impression of a way of life quite different from that of us civilized people. Therefore I am not at all anxious for everyone to like it or to admire it at once.
All winter long I have had the threads of this tissue in my hands, and have searched for the ultimate pattern; and though it has become a tissue of rough, coarse aspect, nevertheless, the threads have been carefully chosen and according to certain rules. And it might prove to be a real peasant picture. I know it is. *But he who prefers to see the peasants in their Sunday-best may do as he likes. I personally am convinced I get better*

results by painting them in their roughness than by giving them a conventional charm. . . .
In the same way it would be wrong, I think, to give a peasant picture a certain conventional smoothness. If a peasant picture smells of bacon, smoke, potato steam – all right, that's not unhealthy; if a stable smells of dung – all right, that belongs to a stable; if the field has an odour of ripe corn or potatoes or of guano or manure – that's healthy, especially for city people.
Such pictures may teach *them something. But to be perfumed is not what a peasant picture needs. . . .*
Painting peasant life is a serious thing, and I should reproach myself if I did not try to make pictures which will rouse serious thoughts in those who think seriously about art and about life. LT404, 30 APRIL 1885

In his next letter, Vincent discusses the picture's colour. He had begun by painting the flesh colour with yellow ochre, red ochre and white:

But that was much, much too light, *and was decidedly wrong.*
What was to be done? All the heads were finished, and even finished with great care, but I immediately repainted them, inexorably, and the colour they are painted in now is like the colour of a very dusty potato, unpeeled of course.
While doing this I thought how perfect that saying of Millet's about the peasants is: 'Ses paysans sembleant peints avec la terre qu'ils ensemencent' (His peasants seem painted with the earth they seed).
A saying which I can't help being constantly reminded of when I see them at work, outdoors as well as indoors. LT405, early MAY 1885

When he packed *The Potato-Eaters* off to Theo in Paris a few days later Vincent was ready for criticism:

In the way of criticism, I myself could point out things which will probably escape most of the critics.
But the reason why I am sending it with a certain confidence is that, in contrast to many other pictures there is rusticity and a certain life in it.
And so, though painted in a different style, in another century from the old Dutch masters, Ostade for instance, it too comes from the heart of the peasant's life, and is original.
Though I see for instance in the salon catalogue so many pictures which, if you like, are faultlessly drawn and painted as to technique, yet many of them bore me terribly because they give me neither food for the heart nor for the mind, because they obviously have been made without a certain passion.
And there is some passion in what I am sending you. LT406, early MAY 1885
1885

In a last attempt to silence Rappard's criticism (see No. 39), Vincent was more self-critical:

As for my work, that scene of the potato-eaters – you saw the lithograph of it – is a subject that I tried to paint, being inspired by the peculiar light effect in that grimy cottage. It is kept in such a low scale of colours that the light *colours, smeared on white paper, for instance, would look like ink stains; but on the canvas they stand out like lights because of the great forces opposed to them, for instance, by putting on absolutely unmixed Prussian blue. My own criticism is that by paying attention to this, I lost sight of the form of the torsos. Heads and hands, however, were done very carefully; and as they were of the greatest importance and all the rest was nearly entirely dark (therefore* quite different *in effect from the lithograph) my painting the picture* as I did *is to be excused to a greater extent than you think. And besides, the real picture differs in design from* either *the rough sketch for it which I still have and which I made in that cottage by the light of a little lamp,* or *from the lithograph.* LR57, SEPTEMBER 1885

Even after his exposure to modern art in Paris, Vincent continued to think highly of *The Potato-Eaters*. In a letter to his sister Wil he said:

What I think of my own work is this – that that picture I did at Nuenen of those peasants eating potatoes is the best one after all. Only since then I have lacked the opportunity to pick my models, but on the other hand I have had the opportunity of studying the question of colour. LW1, AUTUMN 1887

At the end of his life, Vincent's thoughts returned to *The Potato-Eaters*: shortly before leaving Saint-Rémy he wrote to Theo:

I am thinking of doing the picture of the Peasants at Dinner, *with the lamplight effect again. That canvas must be quite black now, perhaps I could do it again altogether from memory.* LT629, 29 APRIL 1890

For his studies of a new *Potato-Eaters*, see Nos. 180–2.

39 The potato-eaters

Plate 32

Nuenen, April 1885
Lithograph, 10½x12 (26·5x30·5)
F1661

Vincent thought that *The Potato-Eaters* subject would make a good lithograph. He was anxious to start making prints again, had found a cheap printer in Eindhoven, and planned a series of scenes from rural life – *les paysans chez eux* (LT400). He was in a hurry: he made the lithograph from the large study before he had finished work on it, and he did not reverse the composition. He hoped to do it again correctly from the final version (LT401); but Theo found the printing woolly and technically unsatisfactory (LT405), and Vincent did not try again. But he had sent prints to Portier, the Paris dealer who was interested in his work, and to Rappard, whose reaction to *The Potato-Eaters* was distinctly unfavourable. His letter (R51A) was extremely patronizing:

You will agree with me that such work is not meant seriously. Fortunately you can do better than that, but why then did you see and treat everything so superficially?

This led eventually and inevitably to the break between the two friends. (See also note to No. 38)

40 Auction because of demolition (The sale of crosses from the cemetery)

Plate 14

Nuenen, May 1885
Watercolour and gouache, 14¾x21¾ (37·5x55)
F1230

These last days I have been working hard on drawings.
They are busy pulling down the old [church] *tower in the fields. So there was an auction of lumber and slates and old iron, including the cross.*
I have finished a watercolour of it, in the style of the lumber auction, but better I think. LT408, shortly after 8 MAY 1885

The watercolour was sent to Theo early in June: Vincent called it, in French, *Vente pour cause de démolition.* LT401, 1 JUNE 1885

41 The old tower at Nuenen

Nuenen, May 1885
Oil on canvas, 24½x30¾ (65x80·5)
F84, H94

Vincent had already painted Nuenen old church several times in 1884, as well as the chapel (No. 19). The old Catholic church had been due for demolition since 1857, and in May 1885 all the movable furnishings were sold (No. 40), and the spire was demolished. The tower in fact remained until 1888, despite what Vincent says:

The old tower will be pulled down next week. The spire has already gone. I'm working at a picture of it. LT408, shortly after 8 MAY 1885

No. 41 has sometimes been identified with the picture which Vincent called in French, *Cimetière de Paysans*, and included in a consignment for Theo early in June. He described it:

I have omitted some details – I wanted to express how those ruins show that for ages *the peasants have been laid to rest in the very fields which they dug up when alive – I wanted to express what a simple thing death and burial is, just as simple as the falling of an Autumn leaf – just a bit of earth dug up – a wooden cross. The fields around, where the grass of the churchyard ends, beyond the little wall, form a last line against the horizon – like the horizon of the sea.*
And now those ruins tell me how a faith and a religion mouldered away – strongly founded though they were – but how the life and the death of the peasants remain forever the same, budding and withering regularly, like the grass and the flowers growing there in that churchyard
'Les religions passent, Dieu demeure' is a saying of Victor Hugo, whom they also brought to rest recently.... LT411, JUNE 1885

Vincent added a note to this letter, asking Theo to varnish No. 41 and its pendant, F83:

The village churchyard especially has sunk in badly because at first I painted it quite differently, and then scraped it off entirely.
At first it was a total failure – then without hesitation I began anew, taking it from another angle and painting early in the morning instead of in the evening. And the other one – that of the cottage – was originally a shepherd.

The identification of *The Old Tower* with *The Peasants' Cemetery* may be correct: in that case, when Vincent talks of sending 'the old church tower' to an exhibition in The Hague (LT421, AUGUST 1885), he must be talking about the earlier version, F88, which shows the tower with its steeple.

42 Peasant cutting wood

Plate 31

Nuenen, May–August 1885
Black chalk, 17¼x21½ (44x54·5)
F1327

One of the series of peasants at work, see No. 43

43 Peasant woman digging, seen from behind

Plate 28

Nuenen, June (?) 1885
Black chalk, 21¾x16 (55·5x40·5)
F1255

Throughout the summer of 1885, Vincent made many drawings of full-size figures, always peasants at work (*cf.* Nos 42, 44–7). There are frequent passing references in the letters:

I am also very busy these days, drawing figures. LT408, after 8 MAY 1885.

I am very busy drawing figures, but I shall have to make a hundred of them before I paint them, as this will save me time and money.
I think they are getting rounder and fuller than at first. LT412, JUNE 1885.

Everyday I work hard on drawing figures. But I must have a hundred of them, even more, before I am through. I want to find something different from my old drawings and to grasp the character of the peasants – especially those from this neighbourhood.
And it is about harvest time, and then I must make a campaign both of corn reaping and potato digging. LT414, JUNE 1885.

I have here before me some figures: a woman with a spade, seen from behind [perhaps No. 44]; *another bending to glean the ears of corn; another seen from the front, her head almost on the ground, digging carrots. I have been watching those peasant figures here for more than a year and a half, especially their action, just to catch their character.* LT416, 6 JULY 1885

I ask you, do you know a single digger, a single sower in the old Dutch school??? Did they ever try to paint 'a labourer'? Did Velasquez try it in his water carrier or types from the people? No. The figures in the pictures of the old masters do not work. . . . *To draw a* peasant's figure in action, *I repeat, that's what an essentially modern figure is, the very core of modern art, which neither the Greeks nor the Renaissance nor the old Dutch school have done. This is a question which occupies me every day.* LT418, JULY 1885

44 Peasant woman digging potatoes, with basket

Plate 26

Nuenen, June–July 1885
Black chalk, 19½x15¾ (49·5x40)
F1251

One of the series of peasant figures at work, see No. 43

45 Peasant digging, seen from behind

Plate 29

Nuenen, June–July 1855
Black chalk, 21¼x16¼ (54x41)
F1302

One of the series of peasant figures at work, see No. 43

46 Peasant reaping, with cap, sickle and hook

Plate 30

Nuenen, June–August 1885
Black chalk, 16¼x20 (42x52)
F1318

One of the series of peasants at work, see No. 43

47 Peasant reaping, with hat, sickle and hook

Nuenen, June–August 1885
Black chalk, 17x22 (43·5x56)
F1316

One of the series of peasants at work, see No. 43

48 Peasant woman shelling peas

Plate 25

Nuenen, July 1885
Black crayon, 16½x10¼ (42x26)
F1214

In April 1885 Vincent was planning a series of lithographs:

I intend to make a series of scenes from rural life, in short les paysans chez eux. . . . *By constantly witnessing peasant life, at all hours of the day, I have become so absorbed in it that I hardly ever think of anything else.* LT400

In the same letter he says that he has 'a great mind to do watercolours and drawings again', and although the projected lithograph series never materialized, there are a number of drawings showing peasants at home made at this time. However, the fact that the woman in No. 48 is shelling peas suggests that it was probably drawn in July, and this may be the drawing mentioned in LT422, written mid-August:

As I told you, I added to this little package of drawings a few new ones, but I shall try to make several more this month, the size of that woman shelling peas, which was the last one I did.

49 Self-portrait, with a pipe

Nuenen, August–November 1885
Oil on canvas, 18x15 (46x38)
F180, H188

One of Vincent's earliest self-portraits, but not a documented picture. It is said to have been painted in Antwerp, but the handling is not like the Rubens' influenced Antwerp portraits (see Nos. 56, 57), and a date towards the end of the Nuenen period seems more probable

50 Still life with apples

Nuenen, September 1885
Oil on canvas, 13x17¼ (33x43·5)
F101, H113

One of several still lifes with fruit mentioned in passing in LT424, late SEPTEMBER 1885

51 Four birds' nests

Nuenen, September–October 1885
Oil on canvas, 15x18¼ (38x46·5)
F112, H127

Vincent collected birds' nests. He wrote to Theo in June 1885:

Tomorrow I am going to paint a spot in another village, also a cottage – in a smaller size. I found it last Sunday, on a long ramble made with a peasant boy to find a wren's nest.
We found six of them, it was a spot that Bodmer certainly would have loved. And they were all nests which the young birds had left, so one could take them without too many scruples. It was so full of character. I have some more beautiful nests. LT411

In the Autumn when he again turned to still life subjects, he painted them:

I am now busy painting still lifes of my birds' nests, four of which are finished; I think some people who are good observers of nature might like

them because of the colours of the moss, the dry leaves and the grasses. LT425, 1 OCTOBER 1885

These still lifes had both a symbolic meaning for Vincent, and allowed him to experiment with colour:

Well, the birds' nests were also purposely painted against a black background, because I want it to be obvious in these studies that the objects do not appear in their natural surroundings, but against a conventional background. A living *nest in nature is quite different – one hardly sees the nest itself, one sees the birds.*
But when one wants to paint nests from one's collection of nests, *one cannot express strongly enough the fact that the background and the surroundings in nature are quite different, therefore I simply painted the background black.* LT428, OCTOBER 1885

52 Still life: pair of boots, with laces

Plate 36

Nuenen, September–October 1885 (?)
Oil on canvas, $14\frac{1}{2}$x$17\frac{3}{4}$ (38x46)
F255, H248

The existence of a still life painting of a pair of boots dated '87 (F333) has led to the traditional placing of this picture at the beginning of the Paris period. But the colours suggest Nuenen, late 1885, as does the evident symbolism of the subject matter – the choice of worn and empty boots offers an obvious parallel with the birds' nests (see No. 51)

53 Still life: with an open Bible

Nuenen, October 1885
Oil on canvas, $25\frac{1}{2}$x$30\frac{1}{2}$ (65·5x79)
F117, H121

Vincent became increasingly interested in colour theory during 1885, as we can see from his correspondence with Theo. There was some discussion about the use of black, with Theo putting forward the impressionist view that it was wrong to use black in shadows. Evidently Theo had to deny that he was prejudiced against black as such, and sent Vincent an analysis of Manet's *Toreador Mort* (now in the National Gallery, Washington), perhaps to show his paint-happy brother how black ought to be used. Vincent writes:

In answer to your description of the study by Manet – I send you a still life of an open – so a broken white – Bible bound in leather, against a black background, with yellow-brown foreground, with a touch of citron yellow.
I painted that in one rush, *on one day.*
This is to show you that when I say that I have perhaps not plodded entirely in vain, I dare say this because at present I find it quite easy to paint a given subject unhesitatingly, whatever its form or colour may be.
LT42, late OCTOBER 1885

The symbolism of Vincent's subject matter is obvious (and perhaps deliberate): candlestick with extinguished candle, family bible open at Isaiah 53, juxtaposed with Zola's *Joie de Vivre.*

III ANTWERP

1885 November 27/28
Arrived at Antwerp, and rented a room near the station at 194 rue des Images. Decorated it with Japanese prints. Impressed by the paintings of Rubens, and especially his handling of colour.

1886 January 18
Accepted at Antwerp Academy, attended classes of Professors Havermaet and Siberdt. Soon quarrelled with their emphasis on line.

February 27
Ill, through overwork and undernourishment. Left precipitately for Paris.

M. E. Tralbaut, in his special study of the Antwerp period (*Vincent van Gogh in zijn Antwerpsche Periode*, Amsterdam, 1948), lists fifteen paintings (portraits and self-portraits, townscapes) and forty-seven sketches and drawings. Antwerp marks the important transition between Nuenen and Paris.

54 Backs of old houses: view from the window of Vincent's room

Antwerp, December 1885
Oil on canvas, 17¼x13¼ (44x34)
F260, H260

I want to tell you that I am glad I came here. Last week I painted three more studies, one with the backs of old houses, seen from my window. . . .
LT438, DECEMBER 1885

55 Old houses, with a view of the cathedral

Plate 34

Antwerp, December 1885
Black chalk on blue paper, heightened with red and blue pencil
9x11¾ (22·5x30)
F1352

Already in Nuenen, Vincent was planning to paint some city views as soon as he arrived in Antwerp (LT433, NOVEMBER 1885). He had some contacts with dealers, and thought they might be saleable. But nobody was interested when he painted 'Het Steen', the old prison on the quayside at Antwerp:

It is just the thing for foreigners who want to have a souvenir of Antwerp, and for that reason I shall make even more city views of that kind. So yesterday I made a few drawings of a spot with a view of the Cathedral. I also made a little one of the Park. But I prefer painting people's eyes to cathedrals, for there is something in the eyes which is not in the cathedral, however solemn and imposing the latter may be – a human soul, be it that of a poor beggar or of a streetwalker, is more interesting to me. LT441, 19 DECEMBER 1885

56 The wet nurse

Antwerp, December 1885–January 1886
Oil on canvas, 20x15¾ (50·5x40)
F174, H147

Although in some ways close to the Nuenen *Heads of the People*, *The Wet Nurse* is on a slightly larger canvas and more broadly handled: this suggests that it was one of the portraits painted soon after Vincent's arrival in Antwerp, when the influence of Rubens makes itself felt

57 Head of an old man with a beard, in profile

Antwerp, December 1885–January 1886
Oil on canvas, 17½x13⅜ (44·5x34)
F205, H225

Vincent hoped to earn some money in Antwerp by painting portraits: even if his sitters wouldn't accept the finished result, at least he did not have to pay for a model. He also had the opportunity of studying Rubens, to discover exactly how he painted his heads:

I am working on my portraits all the time, and at last I have made two which are decidedly good 'likenesses' (one profile [possibly No. 57] *and one three-quarter). That isn't everything, it isn't even the most important thing. But it still seems to me worth while to aim at it, and perhaps it teaches one to draw. Besides, I am getting more and more fond of making portraits.* LT443, JANUARY 1886

58 Skull with a cigarette

Antwerp, January–February 1886
Oil on canvas, 12¾x19½ (32·5x24)
F212, H221

A small study, probably made at the time Vincent was attending classes at the Antwerp Academy.

IV PARIS

1886 February 27
Arrived in Paris, moved into Theo's flat in the rue Laval.
Attended Atelier Cormon, where he met Anquetin, Emile Bernard, Toulouse-Lautrec.

Shortly before June 23
Moved with Theo to a much larger apartment at 54 rue Lepic, Montmartre.

1887 late January–March
Arranged two exhibitions at the Café Tambourin – the first of Japanese prints, the second of the work of Anquetin, Bernard, Lautrec and himself.

May–July
Painted frequently in the Paris suburb of Asnières, sometimes with Signac.

1888 February 20
Left Paris for Arles.

We know less about Vincent's time spent in Paris than about any other period of his life. He was living with Theo, and the correspondence virtually ceases. This is particularly unfortunate, because this was the moment in his career when Vincent moved out of the Dutch backwater into the mainstream of modern painting. He came into personal contact with almost all the leading figures of the day, and learnt much from their work. In this he was greatly helped by Theo, probably the most brilliant and far-seeing young Parisian art dealer of the day.
At first Vincent had to assimilate impressionism proper – he had not been aware of such painting during his stay in Paris, 1887–6, and had seen nothing in Holland. Then in the early part of 1887 he found himself confronted with a choice between two rival *avant-gardes* – that represented by Emile Bernard and Gauguin, whom he met at this time, and that represented by Signac, the associate of Seurat (to whom Vincent was introduced just before he left Paris). Vincent found he could learn from both, and by the autumn of 1887 had attained a personal style which came to triumphant fruition in Arles.

There are about 200 oil paintings and fifty drawings of this period, listed in the De la Faille catalogue. They show a complete change of emphasis. Subject matter is no longer of prime importance – there are no more peasants and workers, far fewer humble objects and familiar landscapes. Instead Vincent paints some fifty flowerpieces, thirty-five still lifes and fifty landscapes – done in part to further Vincent's investigation into colour and brushwork and composition, the abstract qualities of painting.

59 La guinguette: café terrace in winter

Plate 59

Paris, March 1886
Pen, pencil, heightened with white, on grey paper, 15¼x20½ (38·5x52)
F1407

This drawing is closely related to a painting in the Louvre (F238) which shows a waiter and more customers seated outside, and perhaps some foliage on the trees. But the bare trees in No. 59 make it obvious that this is a winter picture, and because the style is dissimilar to works which were executed in the winter of 1886–7, a tentative date of March 1886 is suggested. There are points of connection, in style and subject matter, with Antwerp drawings, and the related painting is certainly pre-impressionist.

60 Still life: plaster cast torso against a light blue ground

Paris, March–June 1886
Oil on canvas, 16⅛x13 (41x33)
F216h, H239

One of several studies of plaster casts, almost certainly done at the time Vincent was attending the Atelier Cormon.

61 Nude study: little girl seated on a chair

Plate 51

Paris, March–June 1886
Black crayon, 11¾x9¼ (30x23·5)
F1367

One of the disappointments of Antwerp was that Vincent found it almost impossible to work from nude models, either privately (LT442) or at the Academy. He greatly looked forward to attending Cormon's studio in Paris, where he knew that life study was taught. Fernand Cormon (1845–1923) was an academic painter who had had great success with scenes from life in the stone age. This study was certainly painted in the Atelier Cormon: such naked children can be seen in Cormon's own paintings.

There is a related painting in the Van Gogh Foundation, F215.

62 Clarinettist and flautist

Paris, March–June 1886
Blue crayon, 10¼x13¾ (26x35)
not mentioned in de la Faille

Soon after his arrival in Paris, it would seem that Vincent made a series of rapid drawings of musicians in a café-concert, using coloured crayons and a sketchbook with large sheets of paper. He had visited café-concerts in Antwerp (LT438), and one presumes continued to do so at first in Paris. Rafaelli was making this kind of drawing for *Paris Illustré* in 1886, and no doubt Vincent was following his example. But these are perhaps the last drawings in which Vincent's ambition to become an illustrator can still be felt: the impact of French painting in 1886 was to turn him irrevocably into a painter.

63 Violinist

Paris, March–June 1886
Blue and green crayon, 13¾x10¼ (35x26)
Not mentioned in de la Faille

See note to No. 62

64 View across Paris from Vincent's room, with the Dôme des Invalides

Paris, late June–July 1886
Black, brown and white crayon, 9x11¾ (22·5x30)
F1387

One of four panoramic views of the Paris rooftops with identifiable landmarks (see also No. 65; also F1388, F1391). These are said to be of the view from Vincent's room, and if so were probably drawn shortly

after Vincent and Theo had moved from the rue Laval to a spacious apartment at 54 rue Lepic in Montmartre. This took place in mid-late June: we know that Theo's lease at rue Laval ran out at the end of June, but A. Bonger's letter of 23 June 1886 mentions the move as already accomplished.
There is a painting of the same view, F261, belonging to the Van Gogh Foundation, probably painted in the summer of 1886.
Theo later wrote to a relative in Holland:

We are living in a rather big apartment in Montmartre, which is, as you know, a suburb of Paris, built on the slope of a hill. The remarkable thing about our dwelling is that one has a magnificent view of the whole town from its windows, with the hills of Meudon, St Cloud and so on, on the horizon, and over it an expanse of sky nearly as large as when one is standing on the top of a dune. LT1a, 10 JULY 1887

65 View across Paris from Vincent's room, with the Opéra

Plate 55

Paris, late June–July 1886
Black, reddish-brown and white crayon, 9x11¾ (22·5x30)
F1390

See note to preceding entry.

66 Still life: flowers in a violet vase

Paris, June–September 1886
Oil on canvas, 24x18 (61x46)
F234, H300

Vincent painted about fifty flowerpieces in the summer of 1886: the choice of the blooms and the background provided a convenient way of experimenting with colour. It is in this period that his palette begins to lighten, and we notice the influence of artists like Delacroix and Monticelli giving way before Vincent's discovery of impressionist painting.

Last year I painted hardly anything but flowers in order to get accustomed to using a scale of colours other than grey – namely pink, soft and vivid green, light blue, violet, yellow, orange, rich red. LW1, AUTUMN 1887

And now for what regards what I myself have been doing. I have lacked money for paying models else I had entirely given myself to figure painting.

But I have made a series of colour studies in painting, simply flowers, red poppies, blue corn flowers and myosotys, white and rose roses, yellow chrysanthemums – seeking oppositions of blue with orange, red and green, yellow and violet, seeking les tons rompus et neutres *to harmonize brutal extremes. Trying to render intense colour and not a grey harmony.*
L459A, written in English to H. M. Lievens, *c.* OCTOBER 1886

It would be interesting to have a botanical analysis of the flowerpieces: this would help establish a chronological sequence, because no doubt each species of flower was available in Paris in 1886 for a relatively short period of the summer. The impasto and residual Dutch colours suggest that No. 66 comes early in the series.

67 Still life: gladioli

Paris, June–September 1886
Oil on canvas, 19x15¾ (47x38·5)
Not mentioned in de la Faille

See note to preceding entry.

68 Quarry at Montmartre

Paris, July–September 1886
Oil on canvas, 22x24½ (56x62·5)
F230, H262

One of several paintings of the semi-rural countryside of Montmartre, obviously painted in the summer, and probably done soon after Vincent and Theo had moved there in late June. In the letter to the English painter Lievens, already quoted (see No. 66) and probably written in October 1886, Vincent says:

I did a dozen landscapes too, frankly green *and frankly* blue. L459A.

69 Boulevard de Clichy

Plate 57

Paris, December 1886
Pen, heightened with coloured crayons, 15x20¾ (38x52·5)
F1393, Cooper 15

The rue Lepic adjoins the Boulevard de Clichy: the leafless trees suggest that the drawing, like the related painting (No. 70) was made in winter time. But an early winter date is more probable — this was the stage at which Vincent was very clearly assimilating impressionist painting, and No. 69 bears this out – the Paris street scene subject comes from Monet and Pissarro, and the two figures cut by the frame from Degas (though the girl on the right is a Renoir girl).

70 Boulevard de Clichy

Paris, December 1886–January 1887
Oil on canvas, 182x22 (46x55·5)
F292, H374

See note to preceding picture.

The drawing is not strictly speaking a study for the oil, because although the street scene is precisely the same, the disposition of all the figures is different. Most notably of course the two girls in the right foreground have disappeared.

71 Woman beside a cradle

Plate 39

Paris, December 1886–January 1887
Oil on canvas, 21¾x18¼ (61x46)
F369, H318

The colour and handling of this unidentified portrait are perhaps closest to the Boulevard de Clichy landscapes (Nos. 69, 70). It also seems stylistically a little earlier than another picture of the same dimensions, No. 77

72 View across Paris, from Vincent's room

Plate 37

Paris, December 1886–January 1887
Oil on canvas, 18¼x15 (46·5x38·5)
F341, H392

A view from the apartment in the rue Lepic: the broken touch is perhaps slightly more advanced than in the Boulevard de Clichy picture (No. 70), though it is too early to discern the influence of Seurat.
Another version of this subject, F341b, belonged to Toulouse Lautrec who made his well-known pastel portrait of Vincent this winter.

73 Holiday at Montmartre

Plate 40

Paris, January 1887
Oil on canvas, 13¾x26 (35x66)
F347, H264

A Montmartre scene, and obviously a holiday time because of the flags. Absence of foliage and warmly dressed figures point to Christmas 1886 and New Year 1887, a date which suits the style.

74 Montmartre gardens in winter

Paris, January–February 1887
Oil on canvas, 13¾x25 (45·5x81·5)
F346, H265

There is no sign of new vegetation, but men are at work in the gardens and it is probably very early in the year. Characteristically in the Paris period, Vincent is less interested in the subject than in technical experiment, and now comes close to the neo-impressionism of Seurat and his friends.

75 The window at Bataille's

Plate 54

Paris, January–February 1887
Pen and coloured crayons, 21x15½ (53·5x39·5)
F1392, Cooper 16

Chez Bataille was a restaurant in the rue des Abbesses in Montmartre, where Vincent and Theo frequently went for meals. The drawing is inscribed and dated, but the overcoat hanging up, as well as the style of drawing (*cf.* No. 69) suggest a date very early in the year. Vincent is now close to Lautrec's drawing manner at this period.

76 Still life: decanter and glass

Paris, February–March 1887
Oil on canvas, 18x13 (46·5x33)
F339, H306

Like *The Window at Bataille's* (No. 75) this is another café interior with a view on to a street, and was perhaps done shortly afterwards. Dated 87, it is also known as *Absinthe*.

77 Woman in the Café Tambourin: La Segatori

Plate 41

Paris, February–early March 1887
Oil on canvas, 21¾x18¼ (55·5x46·5)
F370, H299

The Café Tambourin was in the Boulevard de Clichy, Montmartre: Agostina Segatori was its owner, and a friend of Vincent's.
She allowed him to arrange two exhibitions, one of Japanese prints, probably borrowed from Bing on commission, and the other of the work of Vincent and his friends, Bernard, Anquetin and Lautrec. Vincent writes about this in a letter to Theo from Arles:

When I was in Paris, I always wanted to have a showroom of my own at a café, you know how that fell through.
The exhibition of [Japanese] *prints that I had at the Tambourin influenced Anquetin and Bernard a good deal, but what a disaster that was.*
As for the trouble we took over the second exhibition in the room on the Boulevard de Clichy, I regret it even less: Bernard sold his first picture there, and Anquetin sold a study, and I made an exchange with Gauguin; we all got something out of it. LT510, 22 JULY 1888

We do not know which pictures were exchanged, but as Gauguin left Paris for Panama on Saturday, 9 April 1887, the second exhibition was presumably held not later than March. This means that the Japanese prints were shown sometime between January and early March, probably in February. This gives us a date for the portrait of La Segatori as she is painted seated in her café at the time of the Japanese exhibition.

Vincent also painted some pictures as decorations for the café – possibly the free version of Japanese prints, see No. 78.
He had difficulty in getting them back when La Segatori couldn't pay her debts and went bankrupt. An echo of this affair (of which we know tantalizingly little) can be learned in the two letters Vincent wrote to Theo when he was on vacation in Holland in July–August 1887 (LT461, 462), and in the first letter to Emile Bernard in which Vincent begs him to make up his quarrel with Signac:

I shall be glad to do all I can to make a success of what we began in the café, but I think that the primary condition on which success depends is to set aside all petty jealousies, for only union is strength. LB1, SUMMER 1887

78 Japonaiserie: The Actor, after a woodcut by Kesai Yeisen

Paris, March–May 1887 (or October–December 1887?)
Oil on canvas, $39\frac{1}{2}$x$23\frac{3}{4}$ (100·5x60·5)
F373, H234

The largest, and least familiar, of Vincent's three free copies of Japanese wood-block prints: the others are *The Bridge* (F372) and *The Tree* (F371), both said to be after Hiroshige. It seems possible that these (and perhaps others) were done as decorations for the Café Tambourin in the spring of 1887 (see note to No. 77), but they may date from later in the year.

The question of Vincent's debt to Japanese prints remains obscure and needs further investigation. We do not know for example exactly when and how he first became interested: it must have been in Holland, and seems to come in part from the Goncourts, in part from magazine articles. In addition, Vincent had an uncle who had travelled in Japan. Immediately on his arrival in Antwerp he wrote:

My studio is not bad, especially as I have pinned a lot of little Japanese prints on the wall, which amuse me very much. You know those little women's figures in gardens, or on the beach, horsemen, flowers, knotty thorn branches. LT437, 28 NOVEMBER 1885

As was to be expected, it took Vincent a little time to appreciate the artistic qualities of these Japanese prints – their hard outlines, flat colours, absence of linear perspective and general compositional boldness.

In Paris he visited Bing's shop with its stock of 10,000 prints (LT511), and although unable to afford the more famous names, bought cheaper examples for himself: the Van Gogh Foundation has an uncatalogued collection of about 200 prints which belonged to Vincent and Theo. The taste for Japanese prints was a common bond with Lautrec, and with Bernard and Anquetin, who in 1887 evolved a style, cloisonnism, which owed much to Japanese examples. (See note to No. 77.) Vincent's other great friend at this time, Signac, was not interested.

79 Couples in the park at Asnières

Paris, May 1887
Oil on canvas, $29\frac{1}{2}$x$44\frac{1}{2}$ (75·5x113)
F314, H368

In the spring of 1887 Vincent began to work in the suburbs of Paris, and especially at Asnières, where both Signac and Bernard worked. The blossoming trees suggest an early summer painting, and the style shows Vincent learning about neo-impressionist practices from Signac.

80 Road along the Seine at Asnières

Paris, May 1887
Oil on canvas, 19½x25¾ (49·5x65·5)
F299, H383

The handling and pale colours suggest another early summer painting like No. 79. This is one of the Paris paintings where Vincent's admiration for Monet's landscapes is evident in the subject and composition alike.
In a letter to his youngest sister, Wilhelmina, Vincent wrote:

And when I was painting landscapes at Asnières last summer, I saw more colour in it than before. And I must say that I paint none the worse for it.... LW1, AUTUMN 1887

81 Sailing boat on the Seine at Asnières

Plate 58

Paris, May–July 1887
Pencil, 21x15½ (53·5x39·5)
F1409

Almost certainly drawn in the early summer when Vincent was working at Asnières. Subject and composition stem partly from Monet's paintings of yachts on the Seine.
The colour notes on the drawing may indicate that Vincent thought of making an oil painting of the subject, but no such picture is known.

82 Woodland

Paris, June–July 1887
Oil on canvas, 18x21¾ (46x55·5)
F309*bis*, H347

A high summer painting.

83 Wheat field with a lark

Plate 38

Paris, June–July 1887
Oil on canvas, 21x25 (54·5x65·5)
F310, H360

The state of the corn gives a fairly precise date for the painting.

84 Gateway with a flag

Plate 56

Paris, July 1887
Pen, watercolour and gouache, 12¼x9½ (31x24)
F1406

Sometimes called *14 Juillet* because the flag is out: the date suits the foliage and the style.

85 The walls of Paris, with a horse tram

Plate 50

Paris, July–August 1887
Pen and watercolour, 9½x12½ (24x32)
F1401, Cooper 18

One of four watercolours showing the fortified walls surrounding Paris. Vincent's use of watercolour is here close to Signac's.

86 Shelter with sunflowers

Plate 60

Paris, July–August 1887
Pen, watercolour and gouache, 12½x9½ (31·5x24)
F1411, Cooper 19

Compositionally, this might almost be the pendant for No. 84, with a matching perspectival recession. The subject is again the suburbia of Paris, and there is a closely related painting, F264b. In these pictures, and in some contemporary still lifes, sunflowers first appear in Vincent's painting.

87 View across Paris from Montmartre

Paris, July–August 1887
Oil on canvas, 31½x39½ (81x100)
F316, H364

A high summer painting, with a profusion of flowers in the gardens. This is one of Vincent's largest paintings of 1887 – only the related and clearly contemporary *Garden on the Butte Montmartre* in the Stedelijk Museum, Amsterdam (F350) is substantially larger. It is perhaps these canvases that Vincent was talking about when he wrote to Theo in the summer of 1887 (probably in July or August):

I have done four since you left, and am working on a big one.
I know these big long canvases are difficult to sell, but later on people will see that there is open air in them and good humour. So now the whole lot would do for the decoration of a dining room or a country house. LT462

No. 87 may have been one of the big landscapes which Vincent showed at the Salon des Indépendents in March 1888: the other was certainly the picture now in the Stedelijk Museum, Amsterdam, F350.

88 Still life: fruit

Paris, July–September 1887
Oil on canvas, 19¼x25½ (49x65)
F383, H320

The presence of pears, apples and grapes make it certain that this still life was painted in the summer.

89 Still life: apples

Paris, July–September 1887
Oil on canvas, 18x24 (46·5x62)
F254, H281

Vincent was painting apples at Nuenen in the late summer of 1885 (cf. No. 50), but the style of this picture, and in particular the pattern of brushstrokes radiating around the centre, suggest the latter part of 1887 as a more likely date.

90 Still life: red cabbages and onions

Paris, September–December 1887
Oil on canvas, 19¾x25½ (50x65)
F374, H274

The harder, sharper style is that of the latter part of the year, cf. the two still lifes of apples in a basket, one of them dedicated to Lucien Pissarro. (F378, F379)

91 Self-portrait

Plate 53

Paris, September–December 1887
Pencil, 6½x3¾ (19·5x21·5)
F1379

One of the long series of self-portraits, done in Paris in late 1887. The pose is similar to that in an oil painting in an American private collection, F345.

92 Three self-portraits

Plate 52

Paris, September–December 1887
Pen and pencil, 12½x9¾ (32x25)
F1378

These drawings may be more 'expressive' developments of No. 91.

93 Self-portrait in a straw hat, facing left

Paris, September–December 1887
Oil on cardboard, 16x13 (41x33)
F469, H408

Vincent had painted comparatively few portraits since his arrival in Paris – only a dozen out of nearly 200 pictures. But the concentration on landscape and still life was partly due to his inability to pay for models, and this is perhaps the explanation of the long series of perhaps twenty self-portraits which he painted between September and December 1887.
These are all small paintings, sometimes very small. They show

Vincent in his Paris days to have been conventionally dressed – he is no longer the peasant painter of the Dutch period, and sometimes sports a collar and tie. The straw hat pictures may be earlier than the felt hat ones, but it is difficult to suggest any chronological sequence.

94 Self-portrait, facing right

Paris, September–December 1887
Oil on board, 16x13 (41x33)
F356, H412

See note to No. 93

95 Self-portrait in a black felt hat

Paris, September–December 1887
Oil on canvas, 16¼x13 (42x33)
Not mentioned in de la Faille

See note to No. 93

96 Self-portrait in a grey felt hat

Plate 45

Paris, September–December 1887
Oil on canvas, 17x14½ (45x37·5)
F344, H plate VII

See note to No. 93

97 Still life: decanter, lemons and oranges

Plate 48

Paris, November–December 1887
Oil on canvas, 18x14¾ (46·5x38·5)
F340, H307

Dated 1887, this still life was probably painted towards the end of the year.

98 Still life with books (*Romans Parisiens*)

Plate 46

Paris, November 1887–February 1888
Oil on canvas, (53x72·5)
F358, H230

Books were a lasting passion of Vincent's, and they appear in several of his still lifes, at times with an obvious symbolic relevance (for example *Still Life with an open Bible*, No. 53). Signac, who became a particular friend of Vincent's in 1887, had also painted still lifes with books, and Vincent perhaps knew a small oil of a single yellow-backed French novel, said to have been done in 1887.
This is the smaller of two still lifes of Parisian novels. The colour, though very bright, makes less use of opposing complementaries than most Paris-period still lifes, and this, and the handling, suggest that it was probably done at the end of the two years.

99 Self-portrait: the artist at his easel

Plate 49

Paris, January–February 1888
Oil on canvas, 25½x19¾ (65·5x50·5)
F522, H425

Dated 1888, and painted immediately before leaving for Arles, this self-portrait is the culmination of the series that had occupied Vincent during the later months of 1887.
Vincent spoke of it when he wrote to his sister Wil some months later:

. . . I want to try to paint my self-portrait in writing. In the first place I want to emphasize the fact that one and the same person may furnish motifs for very different portraits.
Here I give a conception of mine, which is the result of a portrait I painted in the mirror, and which is now in Theo's possession.
A pinkish grey face with green eyes, ash coloured hair, wrinkles on the forehead and around the mouth, stiff, wooden, a very red beard, considerably neglected and mournful, but the lips are full; a blue peasant's blouse of coarse linen; and a palette with citron yellow, vermilion, malachite green, cobalt blue – in short, all the colours on the palette except the orange beard, but only pure colours. The figure is against a greyish-white wall. You will say that this is rather like a death's head. . . . well, yes, that's the sort of face it is, and it isn't easy to paint oneself – at any rate, it's

something quite different from a photograph. And you see, this, in my opinion, is the great advantage of impressionism – it is not banal, and one seeks a deeper resemblance than the photographer's. LW4, late JUNE–JULY 1888

It is interesting to note the way in which Vincent builds the colour scheme of the picture around a basic blue-orange contrast.

V ARLES

1888 February 20
Arrived in Arles, took rooms in a hotel near the railway station, the Café de l'Alcazar, Place Lamartine.

March
Two landscapes exhibited at Salon des Indépendents.

May 1
Leased rooms at 2 Place Lamartine, which at first he could not furnish and used only as a studio.

June 17–23
At Saintes-Maries-de-la-Mer, on the Mediterranean.

September 17
Moved into the 'Yellow House', 2 Place Lamartine.

October 25 (?)
Gauguin joined Vincent in Arles.

Mid-December
Gauguin and Van Gogh visited Montpellier to see the Musée Bruyas.

Late December
Theo told Vincent of his engagement to Johanna Bonger.

December 23
Vincent, in a state of excitement and in a high fever, cut off a piece of his own ear and took it to a woman in a brothel. There was a violent scene: Roulin, the postman, got Vincent home, but the police intervened, and sent him to hospital.

December 25
Summoned by a telegram from Gauguin, Theo arrived in Arles. He stayed a few days until Vincent was better, then returned to Paris with Gauguin.

1889 January 7
Vincent left hospital, to return to the Yellow House.

February 5–7 (?)
Second mental crisis forced Vincent to return to the hospital: this was

soon after followed by two more breakdowns. Vincent wrote to his younger sister Wil on 30 April: 'In all I have had four great crises, in which I did not know in the least what I said, what I wanted, or what I was doing. And in addition, before that I had three fainting fits, without any plausible reason, and without retaining the slightest remembrance of what I felt.' (W11) The cause of Vincent's illness was in all probability latent mental epilepsy, an inherited condition, which had been aggravated in Arles by Gauguin's presence and by the news of Theo's engagement.

March 23
Signac visited Vincent in hospital: they went to look at pictures at the Yellow House.

April 17
Marriage of Theo.

May 8
Vincent left Arles for Saint-Rémy, in the company of Pastor Salles.

In just over a year at Arles, Vincent made almost 200 paintings and over 100 drawings and watercolours – mainly landscapes, but also portraits, flowerpieces and still lifes. Never did he paint with such inspiration: these months represent the climax of his career. Subject matter now resumes the significance it had before Paris. For Vincent, 'all reality is symbolic', and every object, every shape, in the paintings has its meaning. No better examples can be seen than the pictures of the two chairs.

On his arrival in Arles, Vincent was overwhelmed by the light and colour of the South. 'I feel I am in Japan,' he told Theo. The spring and early summer were unbelievably beautiful, and by August he felt fully confident of his own powers as a painter. 'What I learnt in Paris is leaving me, and I am returning to the ideas I had at home before I knew the impressionists' (LT 520, 11 August 1888).

But Vincent was now awaiting Gauguin's arrival with growing anticipation, and his worst fears were to be realized. The two men were temperamentally and artistically incompatible. Gauguin liked some of Vincent's pictures, but insisted that he should work in a radically different way – painting from memory and not from nature. Gauguin also disliked Vincent's expressive brushwork, his use of colour, his symmetrical compositions, but Vincent's experiments in Gauguin's manner were not too happy.

In hospital, Vincent was scarcely able to tackle new subjects, and instead made copies of existing works, a practice much extended at Saint-Rémy.

100 Portrait of an old Arlésienne

Arles, February 1888
Oil on canvas, 22x17 (55x43)
F390, H429, SA1

Perhaps the first painting done after Vincent's arrival in Arles on 21 February.
He wrote to Theo a few days later:

So far I haven't found life here as cheap as I'd hoped, but still I have finished three studies, which is probably more than I could have managed in Paris these days....
The studies I've done are – an old Arlésienne, a landscape in the snow, a view of a bit of pavement with a pork butcher's shop.... LT464, *c.* 25 FEBRUARY 1888

101 The drawbridge

Plate 64

Arles, March 1888
Oil on canvas, 23x28½ (60x74)
F400, H436, SA10

Vincent made several paintings of the drawbridge in March 1888.
He told Bernard that the subject attracted him:

... sailors returning with their sweethearts to the town, with a strange drawbridge which stands out in silhouette against an enormous yellow sun. I have another study of the same subject with a group of washerwomen.
LB2, MARCH 1888

He wrote to Theo about the version with washerwomen:

It is a drawbridge with a little cart going over it, outlined against a blue sky – the river blue as well, the banks orange-coloured with green grass and a group of women washing linen in smocks and multicoloured caps.
LT469, *c.* 17 MARCH 1888

Because of bad weather Vincent had to work on the version with sailors at home:

I want to be able to lay on colours like those in stained glass windows and make use of a design in bold lines. LT470, 18 MARCH 1888

But unfortunately he spoiled the picture:

I've had a setback with the sunset with figures and a bridge that I spoke of to Bernard. The bad weather prevented my working on the spot, and I've completely ruined it by trying to finish it at home. However, I at once began the same subject again on another canvas, but, as the weather was quite different, in grey tones and without figures. LT471, *c.* 24 MARCH 1888

No. 101 is this version in grey tones and without figures. It is marginally larger than the picture with washerwomen (F397, in the Kröller-Müller Museum) and two later variants. (F571 and F570) The bridge in the picture, the Pont de Langlois (*not* de l'Anglais), was demolished in 1935, but a copy was built in 1962 about two miles away.

102 Path with pollarded willows

Plate 94

Arles, March 1888
Pen and pencil, 10x13¾ (25·5x34·5)
F1499

Exceptionally, this drawing is inscribed and dated, Arles Mars 1888. Vincent later made a small painting of the subject (F407), which he sent to Theo with other studies:

There is a little landscape with a hovel, white, red and green, and a cypress beside it; you have the drawing of it, and I did the whole painting of it in the house. This will show you that, if you like, I can make little pictures like the Japanese prints of all these drawings. LT484, 7 MAY 1888

103 Two peach trees

Plate 89

Arles, March 1888
Black chalk and watercolour, 18x12
F1469, Cooper 21

This is always said to be a watercolour replica of the picture which Vincent sent to the widow of Anton Mauve, F394, *Souvenir de Mauve.* It is certainly true that he painted a second oil painting, F404 (No. 104 in the exhibition), but it is hard to see why the watercolour should not show us the first idea of the subject and precede the first oil. For one thing, there is considerably less blossom shown on the tree.

104 Orchard in blossom: pink peach tree

Plate 63

Arles, April 1888
Oil on canvas, $31\frac{1}{2}$x$23\frac{1}{2}$ (81x60)
F404, H plate VIII, SA14

This is the centre of the large orchard triptych: see also Nos. 105 and 106.
Vincent began painting the fruit orchards in blossom at the end of March: he told Theo on about 24 March:

I've just finished a group of apricot trees in bloom in a little orchard of fresh green. LT471

The subject rapidly became an obsession, and by the end of the month he had painted at least five, spurred on by his knowledge that the blossom wouldn't last. On 9 April he wrote:

I have another orchard, as good as the pink peach tree, apricot trees of a very pale pink [this is F555, No. 105]. *At the moment I am working on some plum trees, yellowish white, with thousands, of black branches* [F403, No. 106]. LT474

Vincent was now beginning to group the pictures into triptychs, and as he had decided to send the pink peach tree (F394) to the widow of the painter Mauve as a tribute, he needed to paint a replica to serve as the centrepiece. This was F404, No. 104, which gave Vincent much trouble. He explained the scheme to Theo, with a drawing to make his point clear:

You see from the three squares on the other side of the page that the three orchards make a series, more or less. I have also just now a little pear tree, vertical [this is F405, No. 108], *between two horizontal canvases. That will make six canvases of orchards in bloom. I am now trying every day to touch them up and give them a certain unity.*
I dare to hope for three more, matching in the same way, but so far they have got no further than embryos or foetuses.
I should very much like to do this series of nine canvases. You see we may consider the nine canvases of this year as the first design for a final scheme of decoration a great deal bigger . . . which would be carried out on just the same lines, next year at the same season. LT477, c. 10–14 APRIL 1888

By 20 April the series was virtually at an end:

I have ten orchards now, not counting three little studies, and one big one of a cherry tree, which I've spoiled.

When will you be back, and what exactly am I to do about sending things? – for I must get fresh subjects as most of the flowering in the orchards is over. LT478, 20 APRIL 1888

The orchard series has a precedent in Monet's series and his decorative panels, but in general it clearly marks Van Gogh's independence of impressionism. He knew well that trees in blossom were a Japanese motif, and had copied – or invented – a Japanese example in Paris (F371). In Arles where he felt he was in Japan he could expand this idea. The admiration for Japanese prints is evident in both style and subject – not only in the flatness and linear emphasis, but in the frank acceptance of a symbolic, emotional quality which makes Van Gogh's orchards very different from those painted by Monet and Pissarro a dozen years before.

105 The pink orchard: apricot trees in blossom

Arles, April 1888
Oil on canvas, 25½x31¼ (65x81·5)
F555, H578, SA13

The left-hand panel of the large orchard triptych; see No. 104

106 The white orchard: plum trees in blossom

Arles, April 1888
Oil on canvas, 23x31¼ (60x81·5)
F403, H432, SA15

The right-hand panel of the large orchard triptych; see No. 104. There is a related drawing in the exhibition, No. 107

107 The white orchard

Plate 78

Arles, April 1888
Reed pen, heightened with white watercolour, 15½x21¼ (39·5x54)
F1414

Signed and inscribed: *Verger de Provence*, this is a study for, or a copy after, the picture of plum trees in blossom, F403, No. 106 in the exhibition. Vincent mentions it in a letter:

Next the series of orchards – I think that the white orchard of which I'm sending you a pen drawing, and the biggest one in pink and green on absorbent canvas, are the best. F486, 10 MAY 1888

The two paintings referred to are Nos. 106 and 104.

108 Pear tree in blossom

Plate 61

Arles, April 1888
Oil on canvas, 28¾x18 (74x46·5)
F405, H434, SA17

This is the centrepiece of the second, smaller, orchard triptych; see also No. 104. It is perhaps the most Japanese of the series, and was intended to be flanked by the *Plum Trees*, F553, now in the National Gallery of Scotland and the *Pink Apricot Trees*, F556, in the Bührle Collection, both measuring approximately 22 by 26 inches.

Vincent wrote of No. 108:

Here is the other middle piece of the size 12 canvases. The ground violet, at the back a wall with straight poplars and a very blue sky. The little pear tree has a violet trunk and white flowers, and a big yellow butterfly hovers on one of the clusters. To the left in the corner, a little garden with a fence of yellow reeds, and green bushes and a flower bed. A little pink house. There you have the details of this decorative scheme of orchards in blossom that I have planned for you. LT477, *c.* 10–14 APRIL 1888

109 The farm among cornfields

Plate 79

Arles, April 1888
Reed pen, 10x13¾ (25·5x35)
F1415

This is the drawing *A farm by the high road among cornfields* (see No. 114) – of which Vincent has just made a painting when he writes to Theo on 12 May (LT487). It was probably among the roll which he sent Theo on *c.* 1 May (see note to No. 112).

110 Pruning the vines

Plate 80

Arles, April 1888
Pen and reed pen, 10½x13½ (25·5x34·5)
F1420A

Probably one of the drawings sent to Theo about 1 May, see note to No. 112.

111 Landscape with windmills

Plate 93

Arles, April 1888
Pen and reed pen, 10x13½ (25·5x34·5)
F1496

Vincent had long known the work of Alphonse Daudet, and was interested to discover how far he could find reflections of it in the countryside around Arles. This drawing is also known as Daudet's windmill.
It was probably in the roll of a dozen small drawings sent to Theo about 1 May, see note to No. 112.

112 Farm in a field, with setting sun

Plate 95

Arles, April–May 1888
Pen and reed pen, 10¾x13¾ (25·5x35)
F1506

After producing so many orchard pictures, Vincent ran out of money for paint, and during the last ten days of April, while waiting for his monthly remittance from Theo, was forced to spend his time drawing. Although he talks about drawing at times, he had probably made only a few in the first weeks at Arles.

On *c.* 1 May 1888 he tells Theo:

I have just sent you a roll of small pen and ink drawings, a dozen I think. By which you will see that if I have stopped painting, I haven't stopped working. LT480

A few days later he wrote again:

Now the weather is splendid, I have already done two big drawings and five small ones. . . . I am sending the five small drawings to you in Brussels today. LT483, 7 MAY 1888

The subjects were mostly the landscape within easy walking distance of Arles. *The Farm among Cornfields* (F1415, No. 109) almost certainly belongs to this series, with other drawings of the same size and medium, for example F1420A, No. 110 and F1474, No. 114

113 Field with farmhouses

Plate 90

Arles, late April–May 1888
Pen and reed pen, 10x13½ (25·5x34·5)
F1474

See note to No. 112

114 View of Arles with irises

Arles, May 1888
Oil on canvas, 21x25½ (53·5x65)
F409, H442, SA28

Early in May Vincent was working in the countryside around Arles:

I have just done two new studies like this:

[Sketch of F408] *you have a drawing of it already, a farm by the high road among cornfields* [this is F1415, No. 109]

[Sketch of No. 114] *A meadow full of very yellow buttercups, a ditch with irises, green leaves and purple flowers, the town in the background, some grey willows, and a strip of blue sky.*
If the meadow doesn't get mowed, I'd like to do this study again, for the subject was very beautiful, and I had some trouble getting the composition right. A little town surrounded by fields all covered with yellow and purple flowers; exactly – can't you see it? like a Japanese dream LT487, 12 MAY 1888

A few days later Vincent gave another description of the picture to Bernard:

Then a view of Arles. Of the town itself only a few red roofs and a tower are visible, the rest is hidden behind the green foliage of fig trees away in the background: a narrow strip of blue sky is above. The town is surrounded by huge meadows abounding in buttercups – a sea of yellow: right in the foreground a ditch filled with violet irises cuts through these meadows. The grass was cut whilst I was painting. So that it's only a study and not the finished picture I had the intention of making. But what a subject, eh? That sea of gold with a band of purple irises, and in the background the enchanting little town with its pretty women! LB5, late MAY 1888

115 The Crau, seen from Montmajour

Plate 81

Arles, May 1888
Pen and reed pen and black crayon, 19x23¾ (49x61)
F1420

By the end of May, Vincent had perfected his drawing style and was working on a much larger scale. He wrote to Theo:

Today I sent you some more drawings, and I am putting in still another two. These are views taken from a rocky hill-slope, from which you see the country towards Crau (very good wine comes from there), the town of Arles, and the country towards Fontvieilles. The contrast between the wild and romantic foreground, and the distant perspective wide and still, with horizontal lines shading off into the chain of the Alpilles, so famous for the great climbing feats of Tartarin P.C.A., and of the Alpine Club – this contrast is very striking. LT490, 26 MAY 1888

And again to Emile Bernard:

I've done some large ink drawings. Actually two: an enormous stretch of flat country, a bird's eye view seen from the top of a hill, the vines and fields of newly-cut wheat. All that carried on endlessly, the ground stretching away like the surface of a sea towards the horizon, where it is bounded by the little hills of the Crau.
It doesn't look Japanese, yet actually it is the most Japanese thing I have done: a microscopic figure of a labourer, a little train cutting across the wheatfields – those are all the signs of life there are in it.
Now listen: a few days after I started going there I was talking to a painter friend of mine who said, 'That would be a bore to do.' I didn't say anything: I found it so astounding I hadn't even the strength to swear at the idiot. I go back again and again. It's fine! I have two drawings of it – this flat landscape where there is nothing but . . . infinity . . . eternity.
Well, while I was drawing a fellow came up, not a painter but a soldier. 'Does it surprise you,' I said, 'that I find that as beautiful as the sea?' But he knew the sea, that fellow. 'No,' he said, 'I'm not surprised that you find it as beautiful as the sea: but myself I find it even more beautiful than the sea, because it's inhabited.*'* LB10, JUNE 1888

The second drawing referred to is No. 116.
Just over two weeks later, Vincent went again to the Crau to make the painting, No. 118.

116 The Crau, seen from Montmajour

Arles, May 1888
Pen and reed pen and black chalk, 19x24 (49x61)
F1424
Lent by the Trustees of the British Museum.

See note to preceding entry. This drawing is inscribed *La Crau, Vue prise à Montmajour*. It was formerly in the collection of César de Hauke, who bequeathed it to the British Museum in 1968. There is an article on the two drawings by Mrs A. Telleghen-Hoogendoorn, *Geen panorama-landschap bij Van Gogh*, in the Bulletin of the Rijksmuseum, Amsterdam 1964, No. 2.

117 Field with barn and cypress hedge

Plate 92

Arles, May–July 1888
Pen and reed pen, 13x9¾ (33·5x25·5)
F1498

Perhaps one of the small landscape series, see No. 112, though this may have been painted later in the summer. There is no related oil painting.

118 The harvest in the Crau

Plate 66

Arles, mid-June 1888
Oil on canvas, 28½x36 (73x92)
F412, H plate X, SA35

Vincent had to postpone his visit to Saintes-Maries: he had run out of money because he had to buy canvases and pay for the decoration of the Yellow House. So he went out into the Crau, the plain to the east of Arles where he had already made some drawings (see No. 115).

He wrote to Theo on 12 June:

I keep on finding very beautiful and interesting subjects here, and in spite of the worry of the expense, I think that there is a better chance in the South than in the North.
If you saw the Camargue and many other places, you would be surprised, just as I was, to find that they are exactly in the style of Ruysdael.
I have a new subject in hand, fields green and yellow as far as the eye can

reach. I have already drawn it twice and am beginning it again as a painting; it is exactly like a Solomon Konink, you know – the pupil of Rembrandt, who painted vast level plains. [In fact Vincent is referring to Philips de Koninck]. *Or is it like Michel, or like Jules Duprê, but anyway it is very different from the gardens of roses. It is true that I have only been through one part of Provence, and that in the other there is the kind of scenery that you get for instance in Claude Monet.* LT496, 12 JUNE 1888

Vincent was very pleased with the picture, which he thought as good as the *White Orchard* (No. 107), and in the style of the two landscapes of the Butte Montmartre which were at the Indépendents (Nos. 87 and F350). At about the same time he wrote to Bernard:

Today another day of real hard work. I wonder what you would say to my new canvases. You won't find a trace of the timid conscientious brush-strokes of Cézanne. But as, at the moment, I'm painting the same landscape, the Crau and the Camargue, although a slightly different part of it, there may well be a certain similarity in colour. I don't know. Involuntarily I have thought of Cézanne from time to time, particularly at moments when I have realized how clumsy – permit me the word clumsy – is his touch in certain studies. But as half the time I am faced with the same difficulty I can understand why Cézanne's touch is sometimes so very sure and sometimes so clumsy. LB9, JUNE 1888

Some retouching was done about four weeks later before Vincent sent the picture to Theo. This painting and the related drawings, are discussed at length by Dr Mark Roskill in an article, *Van Gogh's* 'Blue Cart' *and His Creative Process*, in *Oud Holland* 1966, No. 1.

119 Seascape: Saintes-Maries-de-la-Mer

Plate 68

Saintes-Maries, 17–23 June 1888
Oil on canvas, 19¾x25 (50·5x64·5)
F415, H454, SA38

At last, at the weekend of 16–17 June Vincent could make his trip to the Mediterranean. He went to Saintes-Maries-de-la-Mer, a village on the coast 25 miles due south of Arles. It gets its name from the two Maries, Mary Cleophas and Mary Salome, who according to the legend landed there in AD 45, with Sarah their servant, and converted the Camargue to Christianity.

I am at last writing to you from Saintes-Maries on the shore of the Mediterranean. The Mediterranean has the colours of mackerel, changeable

I mean. You don't know if it is green or violet, you can't even say it's blue, because the next moment the changing light has taken on a tinge of pink or grey. . . .
I brought three canvases and have covered them – two seascapes, a view of the village, and then some drawings which I will send you by post when I return to Arles tomorrow. LT499, probably written FRIDAY, 22 JUNE

The seascapes are Nos. 119 and F417 in Moscow; the view of the village is F416 in the Kröller Müller Museum. Two of the drawings are Nos. 120 and 121.

120 The beach at Saintes-Maries-de-la-Mer

Plate 82

Saintes-Maries, 17–23 June 1888
Pen, reed pen and pencil, 12x18½ (30·5x47·5)
F1432

Vincent had particularly looked forward to making drawings during his visit to the Mediterranean: he made about a dozen in the week. This is one of those closely related to the seascapes, see No. 119.

121 Cottages at Saintes-Maries-de-la-Mer in sunshine

Plate 83

Saintes-Maries, 17–23 June 1888
Reed pen, 12x18½ (30x47)
F1437

One of the 'rather harsh' drawings of the cottages at Saintes-Maries, see also No. 119.

I do not think there are 100 *houses in the village, or town. The chief building, after the old church and an ancient fortress, is the barracks. And the houses – like the ones on our heaths and peat bogs in Drente* [*cf.* No. 18]*; you will see some specimens of them in the drawings.* LT499, probably 22 JUNE 1888

122 Boats on the beach, Saintes-Maries-de-la-Mer

Plate 67

Arles, 23–30 June 1888
Oil on canvas, 25¾x31½ (65·5x82·5)
F413, H451, SA40

Immediately after his return to Arles from Saintes-Maries, Vincent wrote to Theo:

Now that I have seen the sea here, I am absolutely convinced of the importance of staying in the Midi, and of absolutely piling on, exaggerating the colour – Africa not so far away. I am sending you by the same post the drawings of Saintes-Maries. Just when I was going to start in the morning, very early, I made the drawing of the boats, and I have the picture from it in hand, a canvas of 30 with more sea and sky on the right.
It was before the boats cleared off, I had watched it all the other mornings, but as they leave very early I hadn't time to do it. LT500, probably SUNDAY, 24 JUNE 1888

He wrote to Emile Bernard in Britanny:

At last I have seen the Mediterranean, which probably you will cross before I do. I have spent a week at Saintes-Maries and to get there drove in a diligence across the Camargue with its vineyards, moors, flat stretches of land as in Holland. There, at Saintes-Maries, there were some girls reminiscent of Cimabue or Giotto, slender, erect, a little sad and mystic. On the beach, quite flat and sandy, there are little boats, green, red and blue, so pretty in form and colour that one is reminded of flowers. One man alone can manage them, they don't venture far out. When there is no wind they're off, but back they come if there's even a little too much. LB6, *c.* 24 JUNE 1888

The drawing referred to in the letter to Theo is F1428; Vincent also made an elaborate watercolour of the subject, F1429.

123 The sower, wheat field in background

Plate 84

Arles, 23–30 June 1888
Reed pen, 9½x12½ (24x32)
F1441

The Sower is a theme that often recurs in Vincent's work, from the time that he had copied Millet's *Sower* in the Borinage in 1880. But he had not painted the subject since leaving Holland, but in late June after returning from Saintes-Maries he saw a sower in the fields. He was very anxious to do justice to the subject, but this brought its own problems:

I have been longing to do a sower for such a long time, but the things I've wanted for a long time never come off. And so I am almost afraid of it. And yet, after Millet and Lhermitte, what still remains to be done is – a sower, in colour and large sizes. LT501, 29 or 30 JUNE 1888

The first painting attempted in F422, now in the Kröller-Müller Museum; No. 123 would seem to be a study for it. There is another

similar drawing, of the same size, F1442, which may have been made *after* the painting.
Vincent returned to the subject at the end of the year, see No. 140.

124 The corn field

Arles, 23–30 June 1888
Oil on board, 21¼x25½ (54x65·5)
F411, H444, SA167

Probably done immediately after Vincent's return from Saintes-Maries, when he returned to the harvest theme – here the corn is ripe for cutting.

He wrote to Theo:

I have had a week's hard, close work among the corn fields in the full sun. The result is some studies of corn fields, landscapes, and – a sketch of a sower. LT501, 29 or 30 JUNE 1888

There is a pen drawing, F1481, which is either the study for this painting, or a replica of it.

125 The Zouave

Plate 74

Arles, 23–30 June 1888
Oil on canvas, 25¾x21¾ (65·5x55·5)
F423, H449, SA45

Late in June, Vincent made a break with landscape and began to paint figures again. He told Theo:

I have a model at last – a Zouave – a lad with a small face, with the neck of a bull, and the eye of a tiger, and I began with one portrait, and began again with another; the half length I did of him was fearfully hard, in a blue uniform, the blue of enamelled saucepans, with braid of a faded reddish orange, and two pale lemon stars on his breast, an ordinary blue, and very hard to do. That bronzed, feline head of his with the reddish cap, against a green door and the orange bricks of a wall. So it's a savage combination of incongruous tones, not easy to manage. The study I made of it seems to me very harsh, but all the same I should like to be working on common, even loud portraits like this. It teaches me something and that above all is what I want of my work. The second portrait will be full length, standing against a white wall. LT501, 29 or 30 JUNE 1888

No. 125 is the first portrait of the Zouave bugler; the full-length one F424 was not finished until August and in fact shows him seated. This is not a portrait of Vincent's friend Milliet who was an officer in the Zouaves.

Vincent was not very pleased with this picture, which he called very ugly (LT502). He felt, however, that he must return to studies of figures again. There was talk about exchanging the Zouave's head with one of Bernard's pictures, but Vincent made him a watercolour of it instead, F1482.

126 Wheat field dotted with poppies

Arles, June 1888
Oil on canvas, 9½x14 (24·5x35)
F576, H569, SA109

A landscape not precisely identifiable but close to certain drawings and paintings done in late May and June 1888. It may possibly be the 'little landscape of nothing at all, in which there is only a little expanse' which Vincent also mentions to Emile Bernard as a possible exchange.
LB18, late SEPTEMBER 1888

127 Vincent's house at Arles (The Yellow House)

Plate 77

Arles, June–July 1888
Reed pen and watercolour, 9¾x12 (25x30·5)
F1413, Cooper 23

After living in an hotel near the station for some weeks, Vincent began looking for a house that would serve as the Studio of the South – the centre for the other young painters who he hoped would join him at Arles. He found suitable premises close by at 2 Place Lamartine, on the edge of the town, and on 1 May wrote to Theo, illustrating his letter with a rough sketch of the house:

Well today I've taken the right wing of this complex, which contains four rooms, or rather two with two cabinets. It is painted yellow outside, whitewashed inside, on the sunny side. I have taken it for 15 francs a month. Now my idea would be to furnish one room, the one on the first floor, so as to be able to sleep there. This [house] *will remain the studio and the*

storehouse for the whole campaign, as long as it lasts in the South....
LT480, *c.* 1 MAY 1888

Exactly when Vincent made this watercolour is not known. He did not have any watercolour paints at the time he wrote to Theo: they are requested in a letter of 27 May (LT491) and seem to have arrived in early-mid June. So F1413 was executed sometime between mid-June and September when the painting, No. 136, was made, probably in the earlier months.

128 Corner of a garden, with overhanging branch

Arles, July 1888
Pen, 10x13¾ (25·5x34·5)
F1421

The subject cannot be identified with certainty, but it is similar to that of an oil painting, F428, which Vincent mentions in a letter of 12 July:

Here is a new subject. A corner of a garden with clipped shrubs and a weeping tree, and in the background some clumps of oleanders.
And the lawn just cut with long trails of hay drying in the sun, and a little corner of blue sky at the top. LT508, 12 JULY 1888

The garden was immediately opposite the Yellow House, and Vincent made more studies of it in September (see also No. 134).

129 The rock at Montmajour

Plate 85

Arles, July 1888
Pen, reed pen and pencil, 19¼x24 (49x61)
F1447

This is probably the 'big drawing, but not of the garden' which Vincent made at Montmajour, when he spent a day there with Lieutenant Milliet in mid-July. LT506, *c.* 16 JULY 1888

130 Garden with sunflowers, pail and cat

Plate 86

Arles, August 1888
Pen and reed pen, 24x19¼ (60·5x49)
F1457

I have just sent off three big drawings ... the one with the sunflowers is a little garden of a bathing establishment....

Under the blue sky, the orange, yellow, red splashes of the flowers take on an amazing brilliance, and in the limpid air there is something or other happier, more lovely than in the North. It vibrates like the bouquet by Monticelli which you have. I reproach myself for not painting flowers here.
LT519, 8 AUGUST 1888

131 Landscape with railway carriages, telegraph pole and crane

Plate 91

Arles, August 1888
Pen and reed pen, 9½x12½ (24x31·5)
F1495

Clearly related to a painting, F446, which Vincent calls:

A little study of Paris–Lyons, Mediterranée carriages
in LT522 of about 13 AUGUST 1888

132 Sunflowers

Arles, August 1888
Oil on canvas, 36½x28½ (93x72·5)
F454, H467, SA76
Lent by the Trustees of the National Gallery

In mid-August, Vincent wrote to Emile Bernard:

I am thinking of decorating my studio with half-a-dozen pictures of Sunflowers*: a decoration in which chrome yellow, crude or broken, shall blaze forth against various backgrounds of* blue, *ranging from the very palest emerald up to* royal blue *and framed with thin strips of wood painted* orange.
The sort of effect of Gothic stained glass windows. LB15

He told Theo:

I am hard at it, painting with the enthusiasm of a Marseillais eating bouillabaisse, which won't surprise you when you know that what I'm at is the painting of some big sunflowers.
I have three canvases going – 1st, three huge flowers in a green vase, with a light background, a size 15 canvas [F453]*; 2nd, three flowers, one gone to seed, having lost its petals, and one a bud against a royal blue background, size 25* [F459] *canvas; 3rd, twelve flowers and buds in a yellow vase (size 30 canvas). The last one is therefore light on*

light, and I hope it will be the best. Probably I shall not stop at that. Now that I hope to live with Gauguin in a studio of our own, I want to make decorations for the studio. Nothing but big flowers. Next door to your shop, in the restaurant, you know there is a lovely decoration of flowers; I always remember the big sunflowers in the window there.
If I carry out this idea there will be a dozen panels. So the whole thing will be a symphony in blue and yellow. I am working at it every morning from sunrise on, for the flowers fade so soon, and the thing is to do the whole thing in one rush. LT526, *c.* 23 AUGUST 1888

I am now on the fourth picture of sunflowers. This fourth one is a bunch of fourteen flowers, against a yellow background, like a still life of lemons and quinces that I did some time ago. . . . One of the decorations of sunflowers on a royal blue ground has 'a halo', that is to say each object is surrounded by a glow of the complementary colour of the background against which it stands out. LT527, *c.* 24 AUGUST 1888

Vincent painted another picture of the large bunch of sunflowers, but a few weeks later he told Theo:

I wanted to do some more sunflowers too, but they were already gone. LT543, 29 SEPTEMBER 1888

He did in fact made two replicas in January 1889 after his breakdown.

During your visit I think you must have noticed the two size 30 canvases of sunflowers in Gauguin's room, I have just put the finishing touches to copies, absolutely identical replicas of them. LT574, 28 JANUARY 1889

It is not at all clear when the five extant large sunflower pictures were painted, but Dr Mark Roskill has suggested that the two replicas are F455 (Philadelphia) after F456 (Munich), and No. 133 after No. 132.

133 Sunflowers

Plate 71

Arles, August 1888 (or January 1889?)
Oil on canvas, 37½x28¾ (96x74)
F458, H471, SA77
See note to preceding entry.

134 The pond in the gardens

Plate 96

Arles, September 1888
Reed pen and pencil, 12½x19¾ (32x50)
F1513

This would seem to be a drawing of the gardens opposite the Yellow House which can be seen at the top of the picture. Vincent was painting there in September, see for example his letter to Theo LT541, of *c.* 23 SEPTEMBER

135 Bushes behind a fence

Arles, September 1888
Pen and reed pen, 12½x9½ (32x24·5)
F1477

This also appears to be a drawing made in the public gardens near the Yellow House, see No. 134.

136 Vincent's house at Arles (The Yellow House)

Plate 70

Arles, 22–29 September 1888
Oil on canvas, 29½x36¼ (72x92)
F464, H489, SA84

Vincent had had a lease on the Yellow House from 1 May (see No. 127) but at first used it as a studio, sleeping at the Café de l'Alcazar, also in the Place Lamartine. He did not have the money to furnish it until 8 September when Theo sent him an extra 300 francs: this was used to buy two beds and bedding, twelve chairs and a mirror. After describing his plans for the interior, Vincent tells Theo:

Someday or other you shall have a picture of the little house itself in bright sunshine, or else with the window lit up, and a starry sky. Henceforth you can feel you have your country house in Arles. . . . LT534, SUNDAY, 9 SEPTEMBER 1888

When he had some large canvases at the end of the month Vincent made the promised painting:

Representing the house and its surroundings in sulphur-coloured sunshine, under a sky of pure cobalt. The subject is frightfully difficult: but that is just

why I want to conquer it. It's terrific, these houses, yellow in the sun, and the incomparable freshness of the blue. And all the ground is yellow too. I shall send you a better drawing than this rough sketch out of my head later on. The house on the left is pink with violet shutters, I mean the one in the shadow of the tree.
That is the restaurant where I go for dinner every day. My friend the postman lives at the end of the road to the left between two railway bridges. The night café I painted is not in the picture, it is to the left of the restaurant. LT543, 29 SEPTEMBER 1888

He had moved into the Yellow House on 17 September, and was now excited at the idea of Gauguin joining him in the Studio of the South. A few weeks later he painted the first picture of his bedroom, see note to No. 164.

137 The ploughed field

Arles, late September 1888
Oil on canvas, 28½x36¼ (72·5x92)
F574, H568, SA96

In my last letter I already told you that autumn has manifested itself in rain and bad weather. This has hampered me a little, but all the same I have just finished a size 30 canvas representing ploughed fields; a blue sky with white clouds; an immense expanse of ground of an ashy lilac, with innumerable furrows and clods; a horizon of blue hills and green bushes.... This is another one that will take a long time to dry; pictures that are thickly painted must be treated like the stronger types of wine; one must let them mature. I have ordered a white deal frame for this one. LT541A, *c.* 26 SEPTEMBER 1888

Vincent's friend, the Zouave Lieutenant Millet, approved of *The Ploughed Field* (Vincent's title):

Generally he does not like what I do, but because the colour of the lumps of earth is as soft as a pair of sabots, it did not offend him, with the forget-me-not blue sky flecked with white clouds. LT541, *c.* 23 SEPTEMBER 1888

138 Garden with thistles

Pl. 87

Arles, October 1888
Reed pen and pencil, 9¾x12½
F1466

139 Portrait of Camille Roulin

Plate 73

Arles, November 1888
Oil on canvas, 16x12¾ (37·5x32·5)
F538, H543, SA133

The sitter was the younger son of the postman Roulin, one of Vincent's closest friends in Arles:

But I have made portraits of a whole family, *that of the postman whose head I had done previously – the man, his wife, the baby, the little boy, and the son of sixteen, all characters and very French, though the first has the look of a Russian. Size 15 canvases. You know how I feel about this, how I feel in my element, and that it consoles me up to a certain point for not being a doctor*. LT560, late NOVEMBER 1888

There is another similar study of Camille, F537: this is slightly larger than No. 139, but neither is a size 15 canvas. The portrait of Camille which belongs to the group is in fact F665.

140 The sower

Plate 72

Arles, late November 1888
Oil on canvas, 13x16 (33x40·5)
F451, H480, SA113

This is the small version of a picture Vincent was painting in late October – early November 1888, now in the Bührle Collection, Zürich, F450. There is a little drawing of the composition in a letter of early November where Vincent writes:

This is a sketch of the latest canvas I am working on, another Sower. *An immense citron yellow disc for the sun. A green-yellow sky with pink clouds. The field violet, the sower and the tree Prussian blue. Size 30 canvas*. LT558A, early NOVEMBER 1888

Vincent seems to have made the small version at the end of the month – there is a brief reference in letter 560 where he speaks of being swamped with 'studies' which 'will provide me with some property when I'm forty'. These studies were the small versions, reserved for the family, and Theo acknowledges the receipt of *The little Sower with the Tree* in a letter to Vincent of 22 May 1889 (T9).

The subject of the painting was a constant obsession for Van Gogh (see also No. 123). In this version, the composition with its close-up of the figure cut by the frame and strong diagonal line of the tree, shows the clear influence of Gauguin, then staying with Vincent in the Yellow House, and in particular of Gauguin's 'break-through' picture, *The Vision after the Sermon*, now in the National Gallery of Scotland. Bu the large sun which sits like an aureole behind the sower's head emphasizes that symbolic quality so characteristic of Van Gogh. As he told Theo later:

I feel so strongly that it is the same with people as it is with wheat, if you are not sown into the earth to germinate there, what does it matter? In the end you are ground between the millstones to become bread.
L607, c. 20 SEPTEMBER 1889

141 Gauguin's chair

Plate 75

Arles, December 1888
Oil on canvas, 35½x28½ (91x73)
F499, H522, SA138

This is the pair to No. 142. Vincent first mentions the two canvases of his own and Gauguin's chairs in a letter of mid-December:

Meanwhile, I can at all events tell you that the last two studies are odd enough.
Canvases of 30, wooden rush-bottomed chair all yellow on red tiles against a wall (daytime).
Then Gauguin's armchair, red and green night effect, walls and floor red and green again. On the seat two novels and a candle, on thin canvas with thick pâte. LT563, mid-DECEMBER 1888

And a few weeks later, writing of their mutual friend, the Dutch painter, Meyer de Haan, he says to Theo:

I should like de Haan to see a study of mine of a lighted candle and two novels (one yellow, the other pink) lying on an empty armchair (really Gauguin's chair), a canvas of 30, in red and green. I have just been working again today at its fellow, my own empty chair, a chair of white wood with a pipe and a tobacco pouch. In these two studies as in others, I have tried for an effect of light by means of clear colour; probably de Haan would understand exactly what I was trying to get, if you read him what I have written.
LT571, 17 JANUARY 1889

As so often in Vincent's still lifes, one is made so aware of the presence of the owner or user of the objects that the work becomes a kind of portrait. Vincent had a precedent in the use of empty chairs – Luke Fildes' wood engraving *The Empty Chair, Gad's Hill* made for the Christmas 1870 number of *The Graphic*, of which Vincent owned a copy (see LT220 of July 1882). The circumstances of Fildes' illustration are described, not quite exactly, by Vincent himself in a letter to Theo:

I see Millais running to Charles Dickens with the first issue of The Graphic [4 December, 1869]. *Dickens was then in the evening of his life, he had a paralyzed foot and walked with a kind of crutch. Millais says that while showing him Luke Fildes's drawing* Homeless and Hungry *of poor people and tramps in front of a free overnight shelter, Millais said to Dickens, 'Give him your* Edwin Drood *to illustrate', and Dickens said, 'Very well'.* Edwin Drood *was Dickens' last work, and Luke Fildes, brought into contact with Dickens through those small illustrations, entered his room on the day of his death* [June 1870], *and saw his empty chair; and so it happened that one of the old numbers of* The Graphic *contained that touching drawing,* The Empty Chair
Empty Chairs – *there are many of them, there will be even more, and sooner or later there will be nothing but empty chairs in place of Herkomer, Luke Fildes, Frank Holl, William Small, etc....* LT252, *c.* 10 DECEMBER 1882

142 The chair and the pipe (Vincent's chair)

Arles, December 1888–January 1889
Oil on canvas, $36\frac{1}{2}$x29 (93x73·5)
F498, H521, SA137
Lent by the Trustees of the Tate Gallery

See note to the preceding entry.

143 Still life: a pair of sabots

Arles, January 1889 (?)
Oil on canvas, $12\frac{3}{4}$x16 (32·5x40·5)
F607, H597, SA179

This may be the painting which Vincent mentions in a letter to Emile Bernard – 'a still life of a peasant's old shoes' – 'une nature morte de vieux souliers de paysan' (LB18, end of SEPTEMBER 1888). An alternative suggestion is that this is one of the first pictures painted after the breakdown. Vincent writes to Theo:

I am going to set to work again tomorrow. I shall begin by doing one or two still lifes so as to get back into the habit of painting. LT569, 7 JANUARY 1889

If the latter hypothesis is correct (and the style of No. 143 is consistent with other works of this date) then we should expect a symbolic meaning to the painting: perhaps these are Vincent's own shoes, waiting for him to be ready to walk again.

144 La Berceuse: Madame Roulin

Plate 69

Arles, January–March 1889
Oil on canvas, 36¼x28½ (92·5x73)
F507, H527, SA151

The sitter was the wife of the postman Roulin, and mother of three children, who were all painted by Vincent (see No. 139). He had already painted Madame Roulin three times, twice with her baby, when in December 1888 he began a portrait of her rocking the cradle, as *La Berceuse*. This is a reference to Pierre Loti's Breton novel, *Pecheurs d'Islande* (published 1886) which both Vincent and Gauguin greatly admired. Vincent tells Theo:

When [Gauguin] *and I were talking about the Icelandic fishermen and of their mournful isolation, exposed to all dangers, alone on the sad sea ... the idea came to me to paint such a picture that sailors, who are at once children and martyrs, seeing it in the cabin of their boat should feel the old sense of cradling come over them and remember their own lullabies.*
Now, if you please, it's like a colour lithograph from a cheap shop. A woman in green with orange hair stands out against a background of green with pink flowers. Now these discordant sharps of crude pink, crude orange and crude green are softened by flats of red and green.
I picture to myself these same canvases between those of the sunflowers, which would thus form lamp brackets or candelabra beside them, the same size, and so the whole would be made up of seven to nine canvases.
LT574, 28 JANUARY 1889

Vincent was working on a first version of the subject at the time of his breakdown in December 1888, presumably in part at least done from the model. He painted four more between January and April 1889, at a time when he was suffering recurrent nervous collapses. The later versions are copies of one another; two are dated 1889, but the exact sequence has not been satisfactorily established. One was given to Madame Roulin, and in May 1889 (LT592) Vincent told Theo to offer one each to Gauguin and to Emile Bernard.

The style of the *Berceuse* paintings, with flat areas of colours separated by heavy black outlines, shows the direct influence of Gauguin. Vincent subsequently rejected it, as he told Emile Bernard:

As you know, once or twice, when Gauguin was in Arles, I let myself go into abstraction, for instance in La Berceuse, *or the* Woman Reading a Novel [F497] . . . *at that time abstraction seemed to me a charming path. But it's enchanted ground, and one soon finds onseself up against a stone wall.*
LB21, early DECEMBER 1889

144a The garden of the hospital at Arles

April–May 1889
Sepia, 18x23¼ (46·5x59·5)
F1467

145 Orchard in bloom

Plate 98

Arles, April – Saint-Remy, June–July 1889
Oil on canvas, 29x36½ (73·5x93)
F511, H709, SR 24

Vincent returned to the subject of blossoming orchards in April 1889, but his condition didn't allow him to do as much as he had done the year before. He writes in LT584 of *c.* 13–16 APRIL 1889:

I have six studies of the spring, two of them big orchards –

but whether No. 145 is one of the latter is far from clear. Most were left behind in Arles when Vincent moved to Saint-Rémy, and not collected until 7 July, but No. 145 may be the painting mentioned in LT603 of 6 July:

I often think that next winter I might retouch a lot of last year's studies from Arles. So just lately, having kept back a big study of an orchard which had given me great difficulty (it is the same orchard you will find a variant of, but very vague, in the package) I set myself to work it over again from memory, and I have found the way to express the harmony of the tones more strongly.

An *Orchard in Bloom* was dispatched to Theo around 20 September; Vincent mentions it with approbation in LT607.

VI SAINT-RÉMY

1889 May 8
Vincent was admitted to the hospital, Saint Paul de Mausole, at Saint-Rémy.

July
Visited Arles to collect and despatch some paintings left behind at the Yellow House.

July 10
A fifth, very serious, mental crisis, which left Vincent unable to paint again until the end of August.

September
Vincent now anxious to leave Saint-Rémy and return North.

Mid-December
Another breakdown, followed by two more in January and February. Between attacks, Vincent is perfectly lucid and clear-headed.

January
First article on Vincent's work, by Albert Aurier, appeared in *Mercure de France*.

1890 January 31
Birth of Theo's son, Vincent Willem.

March
First sale of a picture for 400 francs at exhibition of Les XX in Brussels.

May 17
Left Saint-Rémy by train for Paris.

The change of landscape immediately affected Vincent's painting, and new motifs, like the cypress and olive trees, gave him an equivalent for his turbulent emotions. At first he felt comparatively well, but after the July breakdown, the horror of insanity became ever-present, and Vincent knew that there was no cure. He gradually lost faith in his artistic destiny, and painting became a therapy, a means of self-absorption to stave off the inevitable crises.
Almost 150 paintings and 100 drawings were done at Saint-Rémy. Forty of the paintings were copies, and Vincent discovered a new role for the copyist of another's work – that of the colourist. Certainly his palette now attained its most subtle and mysterious range.

146 The stone bench and ivy in the garden

Plate 109

Saint-Rémy, May 1889
Pen and reed pen, 24½x18½ (62x47)
F1522

At first, after his arrival at St Rémy, Vincent was not allowed to leave the hospital grounds, and had to find subjects in the garden. He sketched his first new composition in a letter to Theo, saying that it:

Represents the eternal nests of greenery for lovers.
Some thick trunks covered with ivy, the ground also covered with ivy and periwinkle, a stone bench and a bush of roses pale in the cold shadow. In the foreground some plants with a white calix. It is green, violet and rose ....
Since I have been here, the deserted garden, planted with large pines beneath which grows the grass, tall and unkempt and mixed with various weeds, has sufficed for my work and I have not yet gone outside. However the country round St Rémy is very beautiful and bit by bit I shall go and stay at places probably. LT592, 22 MAY 1889

The highly finished drawing was probably made after the painting, F609.

147 Ivy around a tree in the garden

Plate 112

Saint-Rémy, May 1889
Pen and reed pen, 24x18½ (60·5x47)
F1532

Another garden subject, like No. 146.

148 The fountain in the hospital garden

Plate 113

Saint-Rémy, May 1889
Pen and reed pen, 19x17¾ (48x45)
F1531

Probably drawn soon after Vincent's arrival at Saint-Rémy.

149 Pine trees in the hospital garden

Plate 120

Saint-Rémy, May 1889
Black crayon and pencil, 10x12½ (25x32)
F1570

Vincent sent his brother a roll of drawings on 18 June 1889, and in it there were, as well as four more finished works, a number of 'hasty studies made in the garden' (LT595). It is uncertain whether he is referring to drawings like Nos. 146, 148 and 154, or much sketchier drawings like F1570 and No. 150.

150 Stone bench in the hospital garden

Plate 121

Saint-Rémy, May 1889
Pencil, 8x11½ (30x29·5)
F1577

See note to preceding entry.

151 Chair by a fireplace

Saint-Rémy, May 1889 (?)
Pencil, 12½x10 (32x25)
F1510

Possibly a study made in the hospital soon after Vincent's arrival at Saint-Rémy.

152 Butterflies and poppies

Saint-Rémy, late May 1889
Oil on canvas, 14x10½ (36x27)
F748, H706, SR173

Painted in the garden of the hospital, and with No. 153, one of a group of four small paintings of flowers and insects, all belonging to the Van Gogh Foundation. Vincent mentions them in a letter to Theo:

When I send you the four canvases of the garden that I am working on, you will see that, considering my life is spent mostly in the garden, it is not so unhappy. LT592, 22 MAY 1889

153 Emperor moth

Plate 101

Saint-Rémy, late May 1889
Oil on canvas, 13x9½ (33·5x25)
F610, H608, SR5

Painted in the garden of the hospital, the moth is clearly the Emperor and not the Death's-head as Vincent calls it.

Yesterday I drew a very big, rather rare night moth, called the death's head, its colouring of amazing distinction, black, grey, cloudy white tinged with carmine or shading indistinctly to olive green; it is very big. To paint it I had to kill it and it was a pity, the beastie was so beautiful. I will send you the drawing with some other drawings of plants. LT592, 22 MAY 1889

154 Inside the hospital: window with bottles

Plate 110

Saint-Rémy, May–early June 1889
Watercolour and gouache, with oil, on rose-tinted paper, 24x18¼ (61x47)
F1528

Vincent made three gouaches of the interior of the hospital at Saint-Rémy: No. 154 shows the interior of one of the rooms; the second is a view down the corridor on to which his own room opened; the third is No. 155. There is no mention of these highly finished pictures in the letters – they were probably made early in his stay, when he was still familiarizing himself with his environment.

155 Inside the hospital: the open door

Plate 111

Saint-Rémy, May–early June 1889
Watercolour and gouache, on rose-tinted paper, 24x18¾ (61x47·5)
F1530, Cooper 28

A view from the corridor of the hospital, across a lobby into the courtyard – this is one of the three gouaches mentioned in the previous entry. Beyond the open door can be seen the fountain that appears in No. 148.

56 Stone steps in the hospital garden

Plate 114

Saint-Rémy, May–early June 1889
Watercolour, 24½x17½ (63x45·5)
F1535, Cooper 29

As well as the three gouaches of the hospital interior, there is a series of six watercolours of the hospital garden. They were almost certainly done between 8 May, when Vincent arrived from Arles, and 5 June, when he received permission to work outside the hospital. The others are F1526, F1527, F1534, F1536 and No. 157.

57 Tree in the hospital garden

Plate 115

Saint-Rémy, May–early June 1889
Watercolour, 18¼x24½ (46·5x62)
F1533, Cooper 27

See note to preceding entry.

58 Wheat field with a reaper

Plate 108

Saint-Rémy, late June–early July 1889
Oil on canvas, 29x36 (73·5x93)
F618, H613, SR20

In an early letter from Saint-Rémy, Vincent tells Theo of the view from his room in the hospital:

Through the iron-barred window I see a square field of wheat in an enclosure, a perspective like Van Goyen, above which I see the morning sun rising in all its glory. LT592, 22 MAY 1889

Exceptionally he was in no hurry to paint the view, but waited for the corn to ripen:

For the flowers are short-lived and will be replaced by the yellow wheat fields. Those specially I hope to catch better than I did in Arles. LT593, early JUNE 1889

The opportunity came in June:

The latest [canvas] *I've started is* The Wheat field *in which there is a little*

reaper and a big sun. The canvas in all yellow except for the wall and the background of violet tinted hills. The canvas which is almost the same in subject is different in colouring, being greyish-green with a white and blue sky.
The canvas of The Reaper *is going to be something like* The Sower *of last year.* LT597, between 25 JUNE and 6 JULY 1889

Two canvases of *The Reaper* subject exist – No. 158 and F617 in the Kröller-Müller Museum. Neither fits the picture described above, unless substantial colour changes were made subsequent to the letter quoted. What seems more likely is that one is the full-sized study done from nature which would not have been touched after a day or two's work, and the other is the more carefully painted duplicate, made in Vincent's painting room at the hospital. This was now his normal practice: he writes in a later letter to Theo that he is sending twelve large pictures:

But they will nearly all be the subject twice over, the study and the final picture. LT604

Without having both pictures together, it is not easy to know which is which. Probably No. 158 is the study (which Vincent in fact preferred – see LT608), and F617 the final picture. The former was finished, but not dry, by *c.* 9 JULY (LT600); Vincent was still working on the latter in September, as he tells Theo:

I am struggling with a canvas begun some days before my indisposition, a Reaper; *the study is all yellow, terribly thickly painted, but the subject was fine and simple. For I see in this reaper – a vague figure fighting like a devil in the midst of the heat to get to the end of his task – I see in him the image of death, in the sense that humanity might be the wheat he is reaping. So it is – if you like – the opposite of* The Sower *I tried to do before. But there's nothing sad in this death, it goes its way in broad daylight with a sun flooding everything in a light of pure gold.* LT604, 4 OT 5 SEPTEMBER 1889

159 Wall between wheat field and hills

Plate 118

Saint-Rémy, late June–early July 1889
Charcoal, $12\frac{1}{2}$x$9\frac{1}{4}$ (32x23·5)
F1549

A detailed study, with colour notes, of the distant view from Vincent's window at the hospital. This drawing may have been made while he

was working on the *Wheat field with a Reaper*, No. 158, with which it can be compared.
There is a study of a wooden chair, and of a left-hand, loosely clenched, on the verso: this may have been done several months later.

60 Wheat field with cypresses

Plate 116

Saint-Rémy, late June–early July 1889
Reed pen and pencil, 18$\frac{1}{2}$x29$\frac{3}{4}$ (47x62)
F1538

The conjunction of yellow corn and dark green cypresses inspired Vincent to one of his most memorable compositions. It exists in four versions, which give a further useful indication of his working methods in Saint-Rémy:

1. A full size oil study, F717 in the Bührle Collection, Zürich.
   This was done *sur le motif*, and probably represents one day's painting.
2. A careful pen drawing, No. 160.
   This clarifies the composition and makes possible:
3. The definitive picture, F615 in the National Gallery.
   Here design and colour and brushwork are carefully worked out.
4. A replica in oil, but of smaller dimensions, F743.
   These reductions were made specially for the family. Vincent envisaged making a complete set of his major compositions.

The two large paintings of the *Wheat field with Cypresses* were sent to Theo on 28 September (LT608): this means that they were both completed before the breakdown on *c.* 10 July, as they would otherwise not have been dry enough to send. This drawing must have been done at the same time, but the reduction was painted in September (see note to No. 169).

61 Wild vegetation in the hills

Plate 117

Saint-Rémy, late June–early July 1889
Pen and wash, 18$\frac{1}{2}$x24$\frac{3}{4}$
F1542

This is one of several large pen drawings which seem to have been made in the weeks before the breakdown on *c.* 10 July: No. 160 is another. No painting corresponds to F1542, although the highly convoluted hills do appear in certain oils of this date – e.g., F622 which is mentioned in LT600 of *c.* 9 July:

The last canvas I have done is a view of mountains with a dark hut at the bottom among some olive trees

162 Pine tree and clouds

Plate 122

Saint-Rémy, late June–early July 1889
Pencil, 9¾x12½ (25x32)
F1583

This sketch seems to have been done in the summer of 1889 despite the careful colour notes it relates to no known painting.

163 Undergrowth of ivy

Saint-Rémy, early July 1889
Oil on canvas, 28½x36¼ (73x93)
F746, H629, SR19

Vincent remained fascinated by the undergrowth of ivy on the trees in the hospital garden (*cf.* Nos. 146, 147), and he returned to the subject in July. He wrote to Theo:

I am also working on a new one with ivy. LT603, 6 JULY 1889

And it seems probable that this is the picture mentioned. It must have been finished before the breakdown of *c.* 10 July, which made Vincent unable to work for six weeks or so, because it was dry enough to send to Theo at the end of September (LT608) with a batch of pictures, all done in June and July.
There is a small reduction, one of the pictures made for the family, in the Kröller-Müller Museum, F747.

164 Vincent's bedroom at Arles

Plate 99

Saint-Rémy, September 1889
Oil on canvas, 28¼x36 (73x92)
F482, H627, SR26

Vincent first painted this subject in October 1888, just before Gauguin's arrival in Arles. He describes the picture (F484, in Chicago) to Theo:

... I had a new idea in my head, and here is the sketch of it.
Another size 30 canvas [i.e., 28x36 inches, approximately].
This time it's just simply my bedroom, only here colour is to do everything and giving by its simplification a grander style to things, is to be suggestive here of rest *and sleep in general. In a word, to look at the picture ought to rest the brain or rather the imagination.*
The walls are pale violet. The ground is of red tiles. The wood of the bed and chairs is the yellow of fresh butter, the sheets and pillows very light greenish lemon. The coverlet scarlet. The window green. The washstand orange, the basin blue. The doors lilac.
And that is all – there is nothing in this room with closed shutters.
The broad lines of the furniture again must express inviolable rest.
Portraits on the walls, and a mirror and a towel and some clothes.
The frame – as there is no white in the picture – will be white. ...
I shall work on it again all day, but you see how simple the conception is.
The shadows and the cast shadows are suppressed; it is painted in free flat tints like the Japanese prints. LT554, *c.* 17 OCTOBER 1888

Probably on the next day when some changes had been made, he wrote again:

I am adding a line to tell you that this afternoon I finished the canvas representing the bedroom. ...
This bedroom is something like the still life of the Romans Parisiens [see No. 98] *with the yellow, pink and green covers, you remember it. But I think the workmanship is more virile and simple. No stippling, no hatching, nothing, only flat colours in harmony.* LT555, *c.* 18 OCTOBER 1888

At the same time, Vincent wrote to Gauguin, with a sketch in the letter a little closer to the finished oil than that sent to Theo on the day before:

I have done, still for my decoration, a size 30 canvas of my bedroom with the white deal furniture that you know. Well I enormously enjoyed doing this interior of nothing at all, of a Seurat-like simplicity; with flat tints, but brushed on roughly, with a thick impasto, the walls pale lilac, the ground a faded broken red, the chair and the bed chrome yellow, the pillows and the sheet a very pale green citron, the coverlet blood red, the washstand orange, the basin blue, the window green. By means of all these very diverse tones I have wanted to express an absolute restfulness, *you see, and there is no white in it at all except the little note produced by the mirror with its black frame (in order to get the fourth pair of complementaries into it).* LB22, *c.* 18 OCTOBER 1888

There is no further mention of the subject until 9 June 1889 when

Vincent asks Theo to send him back the study of *The Bedroom* as it has been damaged and he wants to repaint it (letter 594). Theo answers:

I shall send you back The Bedroom, *but you must not think of retouching the canvas if you can repair the damage. Copy it, and then send back this one, so that I can have it recanvased.* T10, 16 JUNE 1889

Vincent seems to have done nothing until after the July breakdown; and when he was able to work again at the very end of August he could not go out of the hospital, and was happy to return to undemanding tasks:

I am working in my room at full speed. It does me good and drives away, I think, the abnormal ideas.
So I have gone over the canvas of my bedroom. That study is certainly one of the best – sooner or later it must be thoroughly recanvased. It was painted so quickly and has dried in such a way that the spirit evaporated at once, and so the painting is not at all firmly stuck to the canvas. That will be the case in other studies of mine too, which were painted very quickly and very thickly. Besides after some time this thin canvas perishes and cannot bear a lot of impasto. LT604, 4 OR 5 SEPTEMBER 1889

Later in the same letter Vincent speaks of making duplicates of certain pictures, including *The Bedroom*, for family and friends.

165 Pietà, after Delacroix

Plate 107

Saint-Rémy, September 1889(?)
Oil on canvas, $28\frac{1}{2}\times23\frac{1}{2}$ (73x60·5)
F630, H625, SR189

This is the first of the many copies of other artists' work that Vincent made in Saint-Rémy between September 1889 and May 1890.
He explains to Theo how he came to make it:

... even when suffering, religious thoughts sometimes bring me great consolation. So this last time during my illness an unfortunate accident happened to me – that lithograph of Delacroix's Pietà, *along with some other sheets, fell into some oil paint and was ruined.*
I was very distressed – so I've meanwhile been busy painting it, and you will see it someday. I made a copy of it on a size 5 or 6 canvas; I hope it has feeling. LT605, *c.* 6–10 SEPTEMBER 1889

The small version on a size 5 or 6 canvas is certainly F757 which measures

$16\frac{1}{2}$x$13\frac{1}{2}$ inches. And there is a reference to the Pietà copy in a letter to Theo from Auvers:

Gachet told me also, that if I wished to give him great pleasure, he would like me to do again for him the Pietà *by Delacroix, which he looked at for a long time.* LT638, 3 JUNE 1890

There is, however, no certainty that any later copy was made, and on balance it seems more probable that F630 was painted in Saint-Rémy.

:66 The Reaper, after Millet

Plate 104

Saint-Rémy, September 1889
Oil on canvas, $17\frac{1}{4}$x$13\frac{1}{4}$ (44·5x33·5)
F687, H674, SR38

One of the series of copies after Millet's *Travaux des Champs*.

The originals were drawn by Millet, engraved by Adrien Lavieille and published in *L'Illustration* for 7 February 1853. (They were also printed separately in 1855.)

The idea of making copies of black and white prints in his possession quickly caught Vincent's imagination. He wrote to Theo:

I have now seven copies out of the ten of Millet's Travaux des Champs.
I can assure you that making copies interests me enormously, and it means that I shall not lose sight of the figure even though I have no models at the moment....
You will be surprised at the effect Les Travaux des Champs *takes on in colour.... I am going to try and tell you what I am seeking in it, and why it seems good to me to copy them. We painters are always asked to* compose *ourselves, and be nothing but* composers.
So be it, but it isn't like that in music – and if some person or other plays Beethoven, he adds his personal interpretation....
I let the black and white by Delacroix or Millet pose for me as the subject. And then I improvise colour on it, not, you understand, altogether myself, but searching for memories of their pictures. But the memory – 'the vague consonance of colours that are at least right in feeling' – that is my own interpretation.
Many people do not copy, many others do – I started on it accidentally and I find that it teaches me things, and above all it sometimes gives me consolation.

Today I tried the Woman Shearing Sheep *in a colour scheme ranging from lilac to yellow. They are little canvases of about size 5.*
LT607, *c.* 20 SEPTEMBER 1889

167 Woman binding sheaves, after Millet

Plate 105

Saint-Rémy, September 1889
Oil on canvas, 17x13¼ (44·x33·5)
F700, H682, SR36

One of the series of copies after Millet's *Travaux des Champs*, see No. 166.

168 Man gathering in corn, after Millet

Saint-Rémy, September 1889
Oil on canvas, 17¼x13 (44·5x33)
F693, H681, SR39

One of the series of copies after Millet's *Les Travaux des Champs*, see No. 166.

169 Cypresses and two women

Saint-Rémy, late September–October 1889 (?)
Oil on canvas on panel, 17x10¾ (43·5x27)
F621, H618, SR163

Vincent began painting this subject late in June:

We have had some glorious days and I have set even more canvases going. . . . Two studies of cypresses in that difficult bottle-green hue; I have worked their foregrounds with thick layers of white lead, which gives firmness to the ground.
I think that very often the Monticellis were prepared like this. You put other colours on it. . . .
The cypresses are always occupying my thoughts, I would like to make something of them like the canvases of the sunflowers, because it astonishes me that they have not yet been done as I see them.
It is as beautiful in line and proportion as an Egyptian obelisk.
And the green has a quality of such distinction. It is a splash of black in a sunny landscape, but it is one of the most interesting black notes, and the most difficult to hit off exactly that I can imagine. LT596, 25 JUNE 1889

The two studies mentioned are F613 and F620; No. 169 is a small version of the latter, one of several of major compositions done especially for Vincent's family. He talks of this idea in a letter to Theo:

I am sending you soon some smaller canvases with the four or five studies that I wanted to give to mother and our sister. These studies are drying now, they are canvases of 10 *and* 12, *small copes of* The Wheat field and Cypresses, Olives, The Reaper *and* The Bedroom *and a little portrait of me.*
That will give them a good start, and I think that it will give you, as well as me, some pleasure for our sister to have a collection of little pictures. I am doing copies on a reduced scale of the best canvases for them....
LT608, 28 SEPTEMBER 1889

No. 169 is much smaller in dimension than the five pictures mentioned in the letter: it may have been done much later shortly before leaving Saint-Rémy.

170 Olive trees (blue background)

Saint-Rémy, late September–October 1889
Oil on canvas, $17\frac{1}{4}$x$23\frac{1}{4}$ (45·5x59·5)
F709, H725, SR171

Vincent began painting the olive groves around the hospital in May. He told his sister Wil:

I have just finished a landscape representing an orchard of olive trees with grey leaves, somewhat like those of the willows in colour, their violet shadows lying on the sunny sand. LW12, early MAY 1889

He continued to work intermittently on the subject until the breakdown in July, and had completed three pictures (including F712) which were dry enough to send to Theo in late September (LT607). About this time when well enough to work out of doors, he took up the subject again:

Unfortunately there are no vineyards here; but for that I should have done nothing else this autumn....
On the other hand the olive trees are very characteristic and I am struggling to catch them.
They are old silver, sometimes more blue, sometimes greenish, bronzed, whitening over a soil which is yellow, rose, violet tinted or orange, to dull red ochre.
But very difficult, very difficult. But that suits me and draws me on to work

right into gold or silver. And one day perhaps I shall do a personal impression of them like what the sunflowers were for the yellows. LT608, 28 SEPTEMBER 1889

The chronological sequence of the fourteen paintings of Saint-Rémy olive groves has yet to be established, but No. 170 was probably painted at this time. See also Nos. 171 and 176.

171 Olive trees in the red earth

Saint-Rémy, late September–October 1889
Oil on canvas, 13½x16 (34x40·5)
F716, H728, SR170

A small study of the olive grove motif, almost certainly done out of doors. See note to No. 170.

172 Entrance to a quarry

Saint-Rémy, October 1889
Oil on canvas, 23½x29 (60x74·5)
F744, H636, SR59

The first version of this subject, F635, was painted in July and sent to Paris with a parcel on canvases in September. Vincent tells Theo:

I rather like the Entrance to a Quarry *– I was doing it when I felt this attack coming on – because to my mind the sombre greens go well with the ochre tones; there is something sad in it which is healthy, and that is why it does not bore me.* LT607, *c.* 20 SEPTEMBER 1889

He took up the subject again a few weeks later:

Then this week I've done the Entrance to a Quarry, *which is like something Japanese – you remember there are Japanese drawings of rocks with grass growing on them here and there and little trees.* LT610, mid-OCTOBER 1889

This picture is mentioned again in a letter to Emile Bernard:

Among these studies there is an Entrance to a Quarry*: pale lilac rocks in reddish fields, as in certain Japanese drawings. In the design and in the division of the colour into large planes, there is no little similarity with what you are doing in Pont-Aven.* LB20, mid-OCTOBER 1889

173 Portrait of a one-eyed man

Saint-Rémy, October 1889 (?)
Oil on canvas, 22x14¼ (56·5x36·5)
F532, H559, SA176

This painting does not appear to be mentioned in the letters and different suggestions have been made for its date. The sitter is not identifiable, and the canvas size is rare in Vincent's work. It has usually been attributed to the Arles period, but the handling and colours are closer to that found in St Rémy pictures after the Summer of 1889. Vincent does in fact tell his mother that he is 'working on a portrait of one of the patients here' in late October 1889 (L612), and although this is usually said to be a reference to F703, it may perhaps be this picture which is mentioned.
Certainly a date of October 1889 fits the style better.
It is possible that No. 173 is the picture included in a batch sent from Saint-Rémy to Theo in Paris late in April 1890. Theo writes to Vincent:

Your consignment of pictures arrived too, and there are very beautiful ones among them. The guard, and the other fellow with his swollen face are extraordinary.... T33, 3 MAY 1890

The guard is the portrait of Trabu, F629, painted in September 1889.

174 La veillée, after Millet

Plate 103

Saint-Rémy, late October 1889
Oil on canvas, 28½x36¼ (72·5x92)
F647, H655, SR91

Vincent is here copying one of a series of four wood engravings, called *Les Quatres Heures du Jour*, made by Lavieille after Millet.
They were published in 1860. The title, *La Veillée*, is untranslatable, as it means an evening spent sitting by the fire at the end of a hard day's work.
Vincent had made drawings after these wood engravings when he was in the Borinage at the very beginning of his artistic career (see LT134: the works themselves do not survive). He now returns to Millet to invent one of his most extraordinary colour harmonies.
He writes to Theo:

You gave me great pleasure by sending those Millets. I am working at them zealously. By dint of never seeing anything artistic I was getting slack and this has revived me. I have finished the Veillée *and have in hand the* Diggers *and the* Man putting on his jacket, *canvases of* 30, *and* The Sower *smaller. The* Veillée *is in a gamut of violets and tender lilacs with the light of the lamp pale lemon, then the orange glow of the fire and the man in red ochre. You will see it; it seems to me, that to paint from these drawings of Millet is much more* to translate them into another tongue *than to copy them.* LT613, *c.* 26 OCTOBER 1889

La Veillée was not sent to Theo until early January 1890 (LT621).

He wrote to Vincent on receiving it:

Do you know, one of the things I like most is that Evening *after Millet. Copied in such a way, it is no longer a copy. There is tone in it, and it is so full of air. It is really very successful.* T24, 8 JANUARY 1890

For Vincent's answer, see No. 177.

175 Autumn, with falling leaves

Plate 100

Saint-Rémy, late October 1889
Oil on canvas, 29x24 (73·5x61)
F651, H657, SR67

This is one of several pictures that Vincent called 'studies of autumn'; it is presumably briefly mentioned in a letter to Theo:

... I have a rain effect going and an evening effect with some big pines. And also one of falling leaves. LT613, *c.* 26 OCTOBER 1889

176 Olive trees (violet background)

Saint-Rémy, November 1889
Oil on canvas, 28½x36½ (73x92·5)
F707, H639, SR75

The highly original colour scheme suggests that this picture was probably one of the last of the fourteen olive grove paintings, done in November 1889. Vincent had been spurred on by hearing that his friends Gauguin and Bernard were working on religious subjects. He wrote to Theo:

I am not an admirer of Gauguin's Christ in the Garden of Olives [W326] *of which he has sent me a sketch. And then as for Bernard's picture, he promises me a photograph. I don't know, but I fear his biblical compositions will make me want something different. Lately I have seen the women picking and gathering the olives, but as I had no chance of getting a model, I have done nothing with it. However, now is not the moment to ask me to admire our friend Gauguin's composition, and our friend Bernard has probably never seen an olive tree....*
If I stay here, I shall not try to paint Christ in the Garden of Olives, *but the gleaming of olives as you still see it ... perhaps that would make people think.* LT614, shortly after 16 NOVEMBER 1889

Vincent goes on to say that he prefers *The Light of the World*, and Puvis de Chavannes' work to Gauguin's religious paintings. In the next letter, written a few days later, he says:

... this month I have been working in the olive groves, because they've infuriated me with their Christs in the Garden *where nothing is really observed. Of course with me there's no question of doing anything from the Bible – and I have written to Bernard and to Gauguin too that I believe our duty is thinking, not dreaming, so that when looking at their work I was astonished at their letting themselves go like that....*
It is not that it leaves me cold, but it gives me a painful feeling of collapse instead of progress. Well to shake that off, morning and evening these bright cold days, I have been knocking about in the olive groves, and the result is five size 30 canvases [i.e. approx. 28x36 in.] *which along with the three studies of olives that you have, at least constitute an attack on the problem. The olive is as changeable as our willow or pollard in the North. You know the willows are very picturesque, in spite of seeming monotonous – they are the characteristic trees of the country. Now the olive and cypress have exactly the significance here that the willow has at home. What I have done is a rather hard and coarse realism beside their abstractions, but it will strike the rustic note and smell of the earth....*
The thing is that they have rarely been painted, the olive and the cypress, and from the point of view of disposing of the pictures, they ought *to go in England – I know well enough what they look for there.*
LT615, late NOVEMBER 1889

There is in fact one small olive tree painting, F714, in the collection of the National Gallery of Scotland, and of course the *Wheatfield with Cypresses*, F615, is in the National Gallery.

177 The snow-covered field (The Plough), after Millet

Plate 102

Saint-Rémy, January 1890
Oil on canvas, $28\frac{1}{2}$x$36\frac{1}{4}$ (72x92)
F632, H686, SR92

Vincent had another breakdown in mid-December, and though he recovered quickly his letters show him rather low in spirits, and not able to work much. Theo's enthusiasm on receiving the painting after Millet's *La Veillée* (No. 174) was a great encouragement:

I am pleased with what you say about the copy after Millet's Veillée. *The more I think about it the more I feel there is justification for trying to reproduce some of Millet's things which he himself had no time to paint in oil. Working thus on his drawings or on his wood engravings is not purely and simply copying. Rather it is translating into another language – that of colour – the impressions of light and shade in black and white. So I have just finished the three other* Hours of the Day, *after the wood engravings by Lavieille. It has taken me a lot of time and trouble....*
... they have their justification in the attempt to make Millet's work more accessible to the great general public....
This week I am going to start on the snow-covered field and Millet's First Steps, *in the same size as the others. Then there will be six canvases in the series, and I can tell you, I have put much thought into the disposition of the colours....* LT623, *c.* 10 JANUARY 1890

The snow-covered field was copied after an etching (by Delauney) of Millet's drawing *The Plough.*

178 White almond blossom against a blue sky

Saint-Rémy, mid-February 1890
Oil on canvas, $28\frac{3}{4}$x$36\frac{1}{4}$ (73x92)
F671, H688, SR85

Theo's son was born on 31 January 1890, and a few days after hearing the news, Vincent wrote to his mother:

I imagine that, like me, your thoughts are much with Jo and Theo: how glad I was when the news came that it had ended well: it was a good thing that Wil stayed on. I should have greatly preferred him to call the boy after Father, of whom I have been thinking so much these days, instead of after me; but seeing it has now been done, I started right away to make a picture for him, to hang in their bedroom, big branches of white almond blossom against a blue sky. L627, 15 FEBRUARY 1890

This was the only painting of the new blossom Vincent was able to paint before suffering his next, and most serious, breakdown, which incapacitated him for two months. He wrote to Theo as soon as he felt well enough again:

My work was going well. The last canvas of branches in blossom – you will see that it was perhaps the best, the most patiently worked thing I had done. painted with calm and with a great firmness of touch. And the next day, down like a brute. Difficult to understand, things like that, but alas, that's how it is. LT628, mid-APRIL 1890

A little later, Vincent wrote to Theo again:

I felt ill at the time I was doing the almond blossoms. If I had been able to go on working, you can judge from it that I would have done others of trees in blossom. Now the trees in blossom are almost over – really I have no luck. Yes, I must try to get out of here, but where to go?
LT629, 29 APRIL 1890

The almond blossom picture seems to have pleased the infant Vincent: Theo writes to his brother that his little namesake cannot yet send him birthday greetings, but:

What he does do is look at Uncle Vincent's picture with a good deal of interest – the tree in blossom especially, which is hanging over his bed, seems to enthral him.... T30, 29 MARCH 1890

179 The sower in the rain

Plate 119

Saint-Rémy, late April 1890
Pencil, $9\frac{1}{2} \times 10\frac{3}{4}$ ($24 \times 27{\cdot}5$)
F1551

After the most dreadful of his mental collapses which lasted from mid-February until mid-April, Vincent began to work again in a different vein. He tells Theo on 29 April:

What am I to say about these last two months? Things didn't go well at all. I am sadder and more wretched than I can say, and do not know at all where I have got to....
When I was ill I nevertheless did some little canvases from memory which you will see later, memories of the North.... LT629, 29 APRIL 1890

This drawing also seems to be a memory of the North – the cottages are like those in the little canvases (F673–5), and the sower harks back to Vincent's own early figure drawings, which in the same letter he asks Theo to send him. It is not I think a scene observed in Provence.
On the verso there is a slight sketch of a Dutch peasant digging, almost certainly executed contemporaneously. Both figures also echo Millet.

180 Dinner for two

Plate 123

Saint-Rémy, late April 1890
Pencil, 9¾x12½ (24·5x32)
F1585 verso

Another 'memory of the North', like No. 179. In the letter quoted under that entry Vincent tells Theo:

I am thinking of doing the picture of the Peasants at Dinner, *with the lamplight effect, again. That canvas must be quite black now, perhaps I could do it again altogether from memory.* LT629, 29 APRIL 1890

He is speaking of course about *The Potato Eaters*, No. 38, to which Nos. 180–2 are related in idea.
On the recto is a drawing of a man and woman walking arm in arm before a Brabant cottage.

181 The meal

Plate 124

Saint-Rémy, late April 1890
Black crayon and pencil, 13½x19¾ (34x50)
F1588

See note to preceding entry.

182 Dinner-time

Plate 126

Saint-Rémy, late April 1890
Pencil, 9½x12½ (24x32)
F1594 verso

See note to No. 180.

On the recto are two peasants digging, in a landscape close to that of the oil paintings, F673–5, the *Memories of the North*.

183 Farmhouse and people walking

Plate 125

Saint-Rémy, late April 1890
Pencil, 9x12¼ (23x31)
F1591

A memory of the North, where the content reverts to Vincent's period as an illustrator.

184 Six studies of a peasant digging

Plate 128

Saint-Rémy, late April 1890
Black crayon, 9½x12½ (24x32)
F1602 verso

One of several sheets of studies of a man digging made at this time, executed from memory.

On the recto, an unfinished landscape study, probably done from nature in the summer of 1889.

185 Studies of peasants working in the fields

Plate 127

Saint-Rémy, late April 1890
Pencil, 9½x12½ (24x32)
F1598 verso

Probably drawn from memory, on the analogy of the figures in Millet's *Travaux de Champs*.

On the recto, a drawing of peasants pushing wheelbarrows in a Brabant landscape.

186 Peasant family around the hearth

Plate 130

Saint-Rémy, late April–early Mary 1890
Pencil, 9x12½ (23·5x32)
F1608

An idea for a figure composition, done from memory but with a clear debt to Millet – *cf.* No. 174, *La Veillée*, for example.

187 Two sowers and six hands

Plate 129

Saint-Rémy, late April–early May 1890
Pencil, 9½x12½ (24x32)
F1603

In the two studies for sower compositions, Vincent seems to place a Millet-derived figure in what is evidently the Saint-Rémy landscape. The hands are presumably those of a sower.

The sketch in the bottom right hand section is done after a figure in Rembrandt's etching of *Lazarus*, which Vincent received from Theo at the end of April, and was about to copy (see note to No. 190).

There are more studies of hands, and of peasants seated and at work on the verso.

188 Study of feather hyacinth

Saint-Rémy, late April–early May 1890
Reed pen and pencil 16¼x12¼ (41x31)
F1612

One of several 'close-up' plant studies, made in the spring of 1890 and recalling *White Almond Blossom*, No. 178, in composition.

189 Study of wild arum

Plate 131

Saint-Rémy, late April–early May 1890
Reed pan and pen, 12¼x16¼ (31x41)
F1613

See note to preceding entry.

190 The Raising of Lazarus, after Rembrandt

Plate 106

Saint-Rémy, early May 1890
Oil on canvas, 19x24¾ (48·5x63)
F677, H699, SR107

This is a copy of part of a Rembrandt etching, one of a number sent by Theo at the very end of April 1890. Vincent was most excited by the *Lazarus*, and immediately painted the subject.

The etchings which you sent me are very fine. On the back of this page I have scribbled a sketch after a painting I have done of three figures which are in the background of the etching of Lazarus*: the dead man and his two sisters. The woman who takes the handkerchief away from the face of the resurrected man has a green dress and orange hair, the other has black hair and a dress of striped green and pink. In the background a countryside of blue hills, a yellow sunrise.*
Thus, the combination of colours would itself suggest the same thing which the chiaroscuro of the etching expresses. LT632, 5–8 MAY 1890

190a Two white butterflies

Saint-Rémy, May 1890
Oil on canvas, 21¼x18⅛ (54x46)
F705, H402

VII AUVERS

1890 May 20
After three days with Theo in Paris, Vincent arrived at Auvers-sur-Oise. He took rooms in the Place de la Mairie, and was under the medical supervision of Dr Gachet.

July 6
Visited Theo and his wife in Paris.

July 27
Vincent shot himself in the chest.

July 28
Theo called to Auvers.

July 29
Death of Vincent van Gogh, aged 37.

1891 January 21
Death of Theo van Gogh, aged 34. The two brothers were buried side by side at Auvers.

Vincent's last months were a time of frenetic activity – seventy oils and thirty watercolours and drawings were executed in fifteen weeks. But he was responding again to the landscape around him, and could still rise to the visionary intensity of the wheatfield pictures.

191 Old vineyard with peasant woman

Plate 137

Auvers, late May 1890
Watercolour, gouache and black crayon, 17x21¼ (44x54)
F1624, Cooper 31

One of the first works produced at Auvers – the influence of Millet persists in the peasant woman. Shortly after his arrival on 21 May Vincent wrote to Theo:

Just now I am very well, I am working hard, have painted four studies and two drawings.

You will see a drawing of an old vineyard with the figure of a peasant woman. I intend to make a big canvas of it. LT648, *c.* 23 MAY 1890

No such large canvas was in fact painted.

192 Houses, gardens and trees

Plate 139

Auvers, late May 1890
Watercolour and pencil, 17¾x21½ (44x54·5)
F1640, Cooper 32

There is an oil painting of the same subject in Moscow, F750, which appears to be the first study that Vincent made after his arrival at Auvers on 20 May (see letter LT636 of *c.* 21 May). He was attracted to the cottages with thatched roofs because they were so close to the memories of the North which he had been painting and drawing in the last weeks at Saint-Rémy.

193 Vase with flowers

Plate 133

Auvers, late May–June 1890
Oil on canvas, 16¾x11½ (42·5x29)
Not mentioned in de la Faille

One of several flowerpieces painted soon after Vincent's arrival in Auvers.

194 Daubigny's garden

Auvers, mid-June 1890
Oil on canvas, 20¼x20¼ (51x51)
F765, H760, SR133

Vincent made several paintings of Daubigny's garden at Auvers. Like Millet and Rousseau, Daubigny stood for a kind of pre-impressionism with which Vincent felt considerable sympathy, and his own emotionally charged landscapes reflect the connection. He was well aware of Daubigny's earlier presence at Auvers, and mentions it in several letters.

195 Two pear Trees with the Chateau of Auvers

Plate 134

Auvers, 16–21 June 1890
Oil on canvas, 20x40 (50·5x101)
F770, H762, SR140

This is certainly the picture mentioned in a letter to Theo which draws attention to the new double square canvas size which Vincent is now using:

Lastly an evening effect – two pear trees quite black against a yellowing sky, with some wheat, and in the violet background the Chateau surrounded by sombre greenery. LT644, 24 JUNE 1890

196 Ears of wheat

Auvers, 16–23 June
Oil on canvas, 25¾x19 (65·5x48·5)
F767, H761, SR134

A painting sketched and mentioned in Vincent's letter to Gauguin:

Look, here's an idea may suit you, I am trying to do some studies of wheat like this, but I cannot draw it – nothing but ears of wheat with green-blue stalks, long ears like ribbons of green shot with rose, ears that are just turning yellow, edged with pale rose by the dusty efflorescence – a rose coloured bind-weed at the bottom twisted round a stem.
Above this, against a very vivid but yet tranquil background, I would like to paint some portraits. The thing is greens of a different quality, of the same value, so as to form a whole of green, which by its vibration, will make you think of the gentle rustle of the ears swaying in the breeze: it is not at all easy as to colours. L643, written between 16 and 23 JUNE 1890

The agoraphobic viewpoint occurs in other paintings of this period.

197 The farmhouse

Auvers, June 1890
Oil on canvas, 15½x18½ (39x47)
F806, H792, SR199

A painting not mentioned in the letters, presumably painted in mid-June.

198 A house at Auvers, with a peasant in the foreground

Auvers, June 1890
Pencil, $17\frac{1}{2}$x$10\frac{3}{4}$ (44x27·5)
F1636

199 Mlle Gachet playing the piano

Auvers, late June 1890
Black chalk on rose-tinted paper, 12x$9\frac{3}{4}$ (31x24)
F1623

A drawing of Dr Gachet's daughter Clementine, made for the painting, F772, in the Kunstmuseum, Basle. The idea and composition were probably suggested by Toulouse-Lautrec's painting of *Mlle Dihau at the piano* (now in the Albi Museum) which was exhibited at the Salon des Indépendents in the spring of 1890. It had been seen by van Gogh, en route for Auvers.

I retain many very pleasant memories of that journey to Paris . . .
Lautrec's picture, portrait of a musician, is amazing, I saw it with emotion.
LT649, *c.* 9 JULY 1890

He wrote earlier to Theo:
Yesterday and the day before I painted Mlle Gachet's portrait which you will soon see I hope; the dress is red, the wall in the background green with an orange spot, the carpet red with a green spot, the piano dark violet, it is one metre in length by fifty wide.
It is a figure that I painted with enjoyment – but it is difficult. He has promised to make her pose for me another time with the small organ. I will do one for you – I have noticed that this canvas goes very well with another horizontal one of corn, the one canvas thus being perpendicular and in rose, the other pale green and greenish yellow, the complementary of rose; but we are still far from the time when people will understand the curious relations which exist between one fragment of nature and another, which all the same explain each other and set off each other. LT645, 27, 28 or 29 JUNE

200 The Mairie at Auvers

Plate 138

Auvers, July 1890 (?)
Black crayon, 9½x12¼ (23·5x31)
F1630

Vincent lived in the Place de la Mairie at Auvers.
The drawing is related to the painting, F790, which shows the Mairie bedecked with flags for 14 July. But the drawing may have been done much earlier.

On the verso is a drawing of an Auvers cottage.

201 Wheatfield with crows

Plate 136

Auvers, 7–12 July 1890
Oil on canvas, 20x40¾ (51x103·5)
F779, H809, SR145

On Sunday 6 July, Vincent spent the day in Paris with Theo and his wife Jo. He returned to Auvers, feeling very depressed and more than ever aware that he was still a financial burden on his brother. Jo had written an encouraging letter, but:

Back here, I still felt very sad and continued to feel the storm which threatens you, weighing on me also. What was to be done – you see, I try generally to be fairly cheerful, but my life too is threatened at the very root, and my steps too are wavering.
I feared – not altogether but a little – that being a burden on you, you felt me rather a thing to be dreaded, but Jo's letter proves to me clearly that you understand that for my part I am in toil and trouble as you are.
There – once back here I set to work again – though the brush almost slipped from my fingers, and knowing exactly what I wanted, I have since painted three more big canvases.
They are vast stretches of corn under troubled skies, and I did not need to go out of my way to try to express sadness and the extreme of loneliness. I hope you will see them soon – for I hope to bring them to you in Paris as soon as possible since I almost think that these canvases will tell you, what I cannot say in words, the health and strengthening that I see in the country.
LT649, *c.* 9 July 1890

The letter may have been written a few days later. Nos. 201 and 202 are two of the big canvases mentioned.

This painting is not in fact Vincent's last work, though the force of the imagery makes it appropriate for that position. Dr Mark Roskill (*Oud Holland* 1966, No. 1) has pointed out that the subject of the painting may be an explicit homage to Daubigny, as it follows very closely certain of his landscape compositions.

202 Fields and blue sky

Plate 135

Auvers, 7–12 July 1890
Oil on canvas, 20x40 (50·5x101·5)
F778, H806, SR144

See note to preceding entry.

Shenval